INSPIRE

INSPIRE

Learning Leadership in the O.R. from One of America's Top Surgeons

By Robert J. Cerfolio, MD, MBA

Printed in the United States of America

ISBN Paperback: 978-1-949639-21-6
ISBN eBook: 978-1-947368-47-7

LCCN: 2017962940

First Edition
23 22 21 20 19 18 1 2 3 4 5 6 7 8 9

Dedication

To my three children—Robert Michael, Alec James, and Matthew Cole—who have become three different types of great and effective leaders.

And to my Mom and Dad for their lifetime leadership lessons they selflessly provided to me.

And, finally, to my wife Lorraine, the love of my life, who taught me more about life and leadership during her battle with cancer then I could have learned in my lifetime. I hope we have made her proud since she passed away on April 14, 2013, at 10:23 a.m.

Contents

INSPIRE

Chapter 1

The Operating Room: A Unique Place to Learn about Leadership

Leadership lessons may be the last things you'd expect to learn from a cardiothoracic surgeon. Leadership? What does a surgeon who's performed 17,000-plus critical operations on the vital organs of the chest have to offer on the subject that would be of any use in your life? When you imagine thoracic surgery, most think about extreme knowledge of human anatomy, surgical techniques and protocols, plus the kind of finely honed motor skills, mental acuity, and grit that enable split-second, life-saving decisions. Some of that is true. You probably don't think of leadership. But surgeons have the mettle to be the best leaders.

Certainly, our work sometimes demands the ability to grab the reins of control and bark out rapid-fire orders. But is that the totality of leadership? The pressure-cooker environment of the operating room (O.R.) has taught us otherwise. Leadership is more than having an imposing title or amassing a collection of skills, abilities, and knowledge. Surgery is a team effort. Everyone on our team must understand the intricate balance between the work of the individual and that of the group. We all realize that along with our technical proficiency and knowledge, the ability to interact smoothly is what has made us one of the top thoracic surgical teams in the world. And the wise exercise—or restraint—of leadership skills is central to optimal team performance.

You may envision that the surgeon's work life is as orderly and sterile as the O.R. itself and as precisely structured as the layout of surgical instruments and robotic tools we utilize. Indeed, it's a job that demands one-hundred-percent focus and attention, along with a highly developed decision-support system, in order to transform knowledge and skill into effective, life-preserving action in the O.R. In some ways, your assumptions about a surgeon's work would be spot on. Many aspects of our daily life are meticulously organized and controlled. Yet, while we routinely use surgical robots quite effectively, surgeons are not robots. We never let our success in the O.R. obscure our mistakes, losses, and failures. They are part of me, as my values propel me to strive for improvement to better serve my patients and my surgical team. In sharp contrast to a business failure or a defeat on the athletic field, mistakes in thoracic surgery can result in the loss of a life—the end of a cherished human being who has family and friends, a person whose life and well-being have just as much significance in the grander scheme as yours and mine.

*

Recently, I was performing a robotic operation with my surgical team, with the usual group of visiting surgeons, residents, and medical students observing. When operating, we strategically insert these little tubes called trocars into the chest. Through the trocars, we place small sponges to soak up blood and allow us to better see the critical structures inside the chest during surgery.

After we completed the major part of the operation, I was ready to start backing out the robot and closing the small incisions. Suddenly, one of my best scrub nurses, Pat, piped up, "Dr. Cerfolio, we've left a sponge in the chest." Fueled by overconfidence due to my assumed habit of knowing the precise placement of every sponge in every operation, my nearly automatic reaction was denial. "No, no, Pat, I don't think so. I'm almost positive we have removed all the sponges." Make no mistake, leaving a sponge in a patient's chest is a bad problem. It would have shown up on x-ray the next day. The patient would then have to be wheeled right back into surgery to have the sponge removed. Serious medical and legal complications might have followed, including a lawsuit—something I've never had levied against me so far, in more than 17,000 operations.

Fortunately, Pat was wise and confident enough to stand her ground. "No, I'm sure you've left one in," she persisted. Despite my initial resistance, I remembered how able Pat is, how well we've worked together, and how much I trust her. So, I placed my ego aside and quickly went looking for the sponge, which indeed had been left behind, just as she said. Problem averted, thanks to Pat, a world-class surgical nurse who knew in her heart that when she needed to exert leadership in a critical situation, she could do so safely, without having to worry about me biting off her head.

Pat felt comfortable speaking out partly because of the culture we have created in our operating rooms, where everyone is a leader and no one team member is more important than another. We all serve the patient, not our egos. This culture makes it safe for Pat to challenge me or anyone else on our team. Had she been mistaken, she knew she would face praise, not blame, for doing her job conscientiously and advocating for the patient's best interest. Pat's example is a reminder that all on the team are accountable—most importantly to the patients on the table who have placed their lives in our hands. We know that's the highest honor there is. When you suffer the symptoms of medical arrogance and overconfidence, resisting the urge to bite off heads is something you have to learn and practice—repeatedly. Yes, situations sometimes necessitate the head surgeon to take command. However, true leadership means remembering that despite our skill and knowledge, we are not perfectly programmed robots. We are just people.

A crucial part of effective human leadership is the ability to see past yourself, to recognize multiple types of input from others on your team, and to alter the course of action as needed. Due to the life-or-death nature of thoracic surgery, this is a lesson unique to the operating room.

Another uniquely surgical leadership lesson arises from the element of risk. Thoracic surgeons specialize in the organs and structures inside the chest. Most of them are absolutely critical to life—including lungs, heart, esophagus, trachea (windpipe), and pulmonary artery, which carries blood from the heart to the lungs, where the blood becomes oxygenated. The risks in cardiothoracic surgery are exceedingly high, and the potential losses can be devastating.

Surgeons feel the unremitting perils of our work every second we're in the arena, scrubbed and sterile, intently focused on helping the person who has put his or her life in our hands. The sense of responsibility is awesome, yet it would serve no one's best interest if we allowed it to distract or overwhelm us, much less inflate our egos and lead to hubris.

Handling the ongoing risk without reducing performance demands intense physical, mental, and emotional discipline. At the same time, it's a balancing act that will fail if our approach is overly rigid. It's imperative to maintain a flexible, open mind in determining the optimal actions and responding to any emergencies that might occur, such as a punctured pulmonary artery or excessive intraoperative bleeding. And that doesn't apply exclusively to the surgeon.

All team members need to be assured and steady every step of the way. They must be able to carry out their roles and responsibilities calmly and with supreme competence, whether in routine functions or in crisis response. There is just too much at stake to behave any other way. We train, study, drill, practice, and test ourselves constantly, all so that we may perform well despite having danger sitting at our elbows.

Thoracic surgery is done in a setting that blends risk and danger with extraordinary levels of skill, precision, and knowledge. Mistakes or poor judgment can occur in the blink of an eye, with dire consequences—permanent consequences. When a patient is lost, you can't just knock back a beer at the end of the day, wallow in self-pity, or console yourself that tomorrow will bring better results. While there are many jobs in which you can feel low, have a bad day, and make it up the next day, cardiothoracic surgery, like many professional jobs, is not one of them. You simply cannot have a bad day in the operating room. Our patients demand and deserve better.

That's why the thoracic O.R. is a unique learning environment. It has taught me why and how to refine my leadership skills and to execute them selectively to minimize risk, improve outcomes, and inspire our team to its utmost performance. But while the O.R. is a unique place, the leadership lessons I've learned there can be used by anyone in any situation, whether you're a CEO of a flourishing company, professional athlete, office worker, caterer, or stay-at-home mom or dad.

*

I began exploring leadership upon realizing that no matter how confident and assured we are as surgeons of our surgical talent, no matter how much we may feel like the top banana, our ability to improve at our job is team-dependent. Yes, we need confidence in our ability to take command in a crisis. But more importantly, we need to remember we can't do it alone. On an imaginary scale that weighed pronouns, "we" would be vastly heavier than "I." In surgery or any other environment, the more that teams work as a cohesive unit, the more successful the endeavors.

Teams, departments, organizations, and families function as systems. By using the tools of leadership properly, individuals can influence the system positively, helping to improve outcomes, profits, efficiency, or working conditions. That's true whether the person demonstrating leadership is an executive with hundreds of subordinates or a blue-collar worker in a limited domain.

The more we learn and refine our leadership skills, the more we are able to motivate and inspire our fellow team members to strive to do their best work. In effect, it's a positive feedback loop. The more I support and encourage my team members, the better they do. The better they do, the more they help me in my role, which in turn makes me a better surgeon, us a better surgical team, and the team more successful as a group. And let's also include the patient as the beneficiary of the team's improvements.

Leadership may be a complex idea but reflecting on it in the context of the O.R. led me to this simple definition: **Leadership is taking your concept and turning it into a team outcome or metric. Outstanding leaders inspire and engage their team members and all stakeholders to embrace that idea and make it their own and turn it from an idea into a reality.**

Exactly how you turn that concept into reality is the trick, of course. Based on my long experience in the O.R. and what I've studied in leadership literature, the heart of effective leadership is a secret that's hiding in plain sight: **Great leaders inspire people to be the absolute best they can be, to strive ever higher as they share values and pursue common goals that are much greater and laudable then personal goals.**

You can be a boss and a leader in any endeavor and can succeed in achieving the designated goals, be they financial, political, or social. Perhaps because I'm in a helping profession, I believe there's much more than power and control to being a great leader—or to being a great team member who demonstrates leadership qualities.

*

So, how, specifically, do we turn a team concept into a team outcome and inspire team members to perform at the top of their game? In the O.R. environment, we all learn to tap into our best leadership qualities and use them to find ways to improve the process of surgery. We don't obsess about the outcome, though in cardiothoracic surgery that outcome always looms large because the patient is foremost in our minds. Surgery is an outcomes-oriented job, as are many jobs in our society these days.

Instead of focusing on outcome, we work as a team to improve the processes of the systems, techniques, skills, and attitudes that will lead to a good outcome. We track and evaluate our outcomes, but we concentrate on process, not product. The more we improve the processes, the better the odds of attaining good outcomes and reaching our goals. In addition, all aspects of our work will improve when we recognize the valuable contributions of people working at all functions, even if their skills, training, and paychecks are not equivalent to ours. Great leadership relies on this team concept.

I recall one typically long day in the surgery theater, my team and I ran into a sort of logjam between the fifth and sixth operations. We still had another five patients awaiting their operations (we use three operating rooms), and I had an important meeting later in the day. Things were falling behind schedule. We're all acutely aware of the rippling negative effects of delays and generally do everything that's safely possible to stay on track.

In order to catch up and get back on schedule, we needed to pick up the pace, but in a way that would not adversely impact the patients or operations. Out of necessity, my attention must remain on the medical issues, and I don't have the time or ability to coordinate logistics away from the operating table. Thankfully, I didn't have to.

A janitor observed the situation, knew my schedule, and figured out how to get things rolling again. He is not a supervisor; no one reports to him. He isn't obligated to do anything outside his basic job description nor to engage in a speedup of his duties. Nevertheless, he cheerfully took it upon himself to do what he could, single-handedly initiating a solution. He called upon several of the custodial staff to gear up for the job. "C'mon," he said, "let's hurry it up to get this room cleaned and ready for Doc Cerf. He needs to get work done and get to a meeting. Let's help get this show back on the road."

The staff responded energetically. Now, he doesn't have a managerial role and still showed fantastic leadership. He went above and beyond, paying attention to what was going on around him. He got involved, even though he could have just shrugged and walked away. Committed to the mission and values of the hospital, driven by his respect for the surgical team, he didn't hesitate to step outside his bailiwick. He saw himself—and rightly so—as a member of the team. He applied his leadership skills to turn the team concept into a team outcome by motivating and inspiring his peers to rise to the occasion.

*

I firmly believe in the power of the team. A strong team with the right kind of foundation can evoke maximum performance and maximum satisfaction to its members, creating a better product or service for its patients, clients, or customers.

A lifelong athlete, I played three sports in high school and baseball in college. Perhaps more than most other team sports, baseball offers the perfect examples of the balance you need to find between individual and team play. As an individual, you have to train and practice relentlessly, developing your skills to the peak of excellence. You must be willing to put yourself out there, exposed before players and spectators, in a game that's defined more by individual failures than successes. A batter with a .300 average is hitting spectacularly well and, yet, is still failing more than succeeding. Yes, it takes humility and grace to put yourself out there again and again and face failure repeatedly. But sticking with it also takes the sort of leadership that can be tremendously inspiring to others.

In the end, though, baseball, like surgery, is a team sport, and you need to recognize how you serve in both capacities—team member and individual player. As a team member, you have to learn all the plays and signs and follow them religiously, never deviating to do what you personally think would be better. If you get pulled from the pitcher's mound for a reliever in the bull pen, or benched game after game, you have to be an equally strong team player. Often times, a bunt or hitting behind a runner at second to advance him to third may help the team win but hurt your own personal stats.

You can show as much leadership on the bench as you do on the field. I love watching the college baseball playoffs and World Series! All the athletes, even those who rarely see playing time, stand at the fence, cheering for their teammates. I see this as my youngest son Matthew plays his freshman year at Columbia and has started at third base. And now that my oldest son, Robby, is working in the front office of the Cleveland Indians, I also see team sports from the business management perspective, not just that of players and coaches. It's no surprise high school and college athletes grow into adults with great discipline, commitment, and strong sense of team and community.

In my experience, there are several qualities or character traits that you can cultivate and practice to develop and enhance your leadership skills. I'll list some below and discuss them in relation to the leadership lessons throughout the book.

Some Characteristics of a Leader

- **Communication Skills:** Be a great communicator in both listening and speaking.
- **Vision**: Know what it means for you and your organization to succeed.
- **Trustworthiness**: To lead at any level, you must earn people's trust.
- **Competence**: Learn your job. If you are not competent at what you do, you cannot lead. Don't try to fake it.
- **Humility**: You can be confident and humble simultaneously. Respect the inherent worth of all people.
- **Awareness**: This includes self-awareness as well as developing heightened awareness and emotional intelligence to fully understand what others are saying and see things from their perspectives.
- **Authenticity**: Clarify your values and be true to yourself.
- **Passion**: Love what you're doing and give it your full energy and attention.
- **Positive Attitude**: Be upbeat and enthusiastic and you will create positive energy around you.
- **Service**: Be a servant-leader. Honor your service as a team member first and a leader second.

- **Courageousness:** Have the strength to speak up for what you believe is right.
- **Accountability**: Acknowledge mistakes. Don't waste time with blame for yourself or others. Take responsibility and move on to solutions.

Your work may not have the same life-or-death urgency as thoracic surgery. Maybe you're a manager at an investment firm, a college basketball coach, or a mother busy managing your family life. Your workday may involve crunching numbers in a spreadsheet instead of using robotic instruments to help you get around a pulmonary artery to remove lung cancer in someone's chest. I can't teach you in this book how to perform a lobectomy (remove a section of lung) in a cancer patient. What we will share with you are the unique lessons the O.R. has taught me about improving my own leadership skills and how that has helped me become a better surgeon, a better father, a better athlete, a better man. The lessons I've learned from my vocation are accessible and available to improve your quality of life at work, home, and play. You can practice what I like to think of as strength training for your leadership muscles. I'll show you how to identify and hone the traits, values, and skills so that you may bring your own leadership to the table in everyday situations. Not only will that make you more effective in all aspects of your life, it will also help you find a greater sense of satisfaction, meaning, and value in your daily life, and, ultimately, more happiness.

CHAPTER 2

LOVE WHAT YOU DO: THE HAPPINESS FACTOR

You may hold a senior executive position with a global corporation. You may pull down $100 million a year and have hundreds of people reporting to you. You may be a school superintendent, an NBA coach, a chief in a city police department. You may be elected to the highest office in the land. You may be supremely competent in your field, a prizewinner, an achiever of goals. No matter your string of accomplishments, **it is hard to be a great leader unless you love what you do**.

This is passion, and you can apply it to your work and all aspects of your life to grow into a great leader—with or without a title. Passion is not a must-have to attain a leadership position with a fat paycheck and power over the lives of others. However, without that deep commitment and love for your work and the people around you, the mark of a great leader who captures the hearts of coworkers will always elude you. Being a great leader is about who you are and what you do, not what you acquire. Remember this description: **Great leaders inspire people to be the absolute best they can be, to strive ever higher as they share values and pursue common goals of others in their organization. Great leaders believe there is far more to success than mere profits.**

In 2005, the late Steve Jobs, co-founder and CEO of Apple, talked about vocational passion in a commencement address at Stanford University. He said: "Your work is going to fill a large part of your life, and the only way to be truly satisfied is to do what you believe is great work, and the only way to do great work is to love what you do. If you haven't found it yet, keep looking. Don't settle. As with all matters of the heart, you'll know when you find it. And, like any great relationship, it just gets better and better as the years roll on." The key is to find new ways to make your job as interesting and fresh as you can.

Among other things, finding your passion and loving what you do will:

- Free up more of your energy, attention, and focus;
- Improve your level of competence at work;
- Help you advance from good to great on the leadership scale;
- Open doors to new opportunities;
- Allow you to actively seek new opportunities in the marketplace;

- Increase your self-awareness and ability to see other viewpoints; and
- Make you happier and better adjusted.

Finding your passion will not transport you magically to fantasyland. Our society is steeped in romantic notions of "happily ever after" and "dreams always come true." Now, far be it from me to crush your aspirations; on the contrary, I urge you to categorically define your dreams and map out a route to transform them into reality. Just don't expect the course to be free of pitfalls and struggle. If an unexpected avenue appears, don't be afraid to take a chance on it. A positive attitude will help you reframe difficulties into opportunities, but it will not make overcoming obstacles easy. And that's okay. You can love what you do even when what you're doing is tough.

Strategies for Learning to Love What You Do

We all want the best for ourselves and our families, so it's natural to grab for the brass ring. Sometimes you'll snag it; sometimes you won't. When you don't, you experience disappointment. When a critical mass of your co-workers feels disappointed, a pervasive negativity may arise. It won't take long for complaining, jealousy, resentment, gossip, and feelings of inequity to poison the water. As an individual and leader in this type of environment, how can you adhere to your core values, stay positive, and love what you do?

Cultivate Self-Awareness

Start by cultivating self-awareness, being honest with yourself, and learning to better understand those around you. With greater awareness, you'll see that getting the brass ring is an outcome, an end product. I encourage every employee to take what's called a 360-degree evaluation. Have all of your colleagues, above and below (bosses, subordinates, and peers), evaluate you anonymously. It may not be easy to accept the results, but it's a tremendous opportunity to improve your self-awareness of how others perceive and respond to you.

These days, people frequently have a cart-before-the-horse approach, which leads to widespread misunderstanding of how to best achieve goals and good outcomes. We want our team to win so badly that we justify any means to achieving the end. In sports, we see how steroids, modified bats, growth hormones, or excessive greed di-

> **Strategies to Love What You Do:**
>
> Cultivate Self-Awareness
>
> Prioritize Process
>
> Take Time to Remember
>
> Keep Life in Perspective
>
> Ask Yourself, "What's My Calling?"
>
> Be Aware of Symptoms of Burnout
>
> Actively and Frequently Retool Your Plans for Happiness
>
> Allow Evolution in Your Job – Reinvent Yourself Every Seven Years

minish the joys of the game for athletes, coaches, and fans alike. In our own lives, we need to be honest with ourselves about the ethical nature, intent, and impact of our words and actions.

Prioritize Process, Not Just Outcomes

Nowhere is the need to prioritize process more evident than in the operating room. Competent surgical teams are hyper-aware that perfecting processes is the only surefire way to improve outcomes. This means looking for potential process improvements in the clinic preoperatively, in the operating room itself, and post-operatively on the hospital floors, recovery rooms, or intensive care units. We collect outcomes data like crazy, but what we're really studying are the inputs—the processes, costs, technologies, and other factors involved in surgery—and how they influence outcomes. We are rich in data but poor in actionable information. As a result, every system, procedure, and instrument in the O.R. is designed, planned, laid out, and followed with enormous precision.

We review, train, practice, conduct emergency drills, and strive for continual quality control because we understand that constantly improving our processes is the best road to achieving better outcomes. You can apply this principle to whatever your field of work. Don't get distracted by the negativity that grows out of disappointment. Staying focused on improving processes—including how your group, department, or organization functions as a team—will leave you less vulnerable to apathy and demoralization. You'll also find yourself much better able to love what you do, which, by the way, is one of the inputs that positively influences outcomes.

Take Time to Remember

It's remarkably easy to get so lost in work demands and pressures that we forget what we love about doing our jobs. To combat this, take up the art of remembering—a practice that's actually tougher than it sounds. Establish a regular habit of pausing for a moment to remember why you got into your field, one aspect of the job that you love, or some other way that you find your work gratifying.

Personally, I take about twenty to thirty seconds early every morning, after my hurried breakfast, to remind myself that my work truly is fun. I reflect on what an incredible honor it is to have six or eight patients each day who trust me to operate on them and improve the quality of their health. One day I will not be able to do surgery anymore. For those times when you lose track of the ground under your feet, quick little rituals such as this are stabilizing, restorative, and invigorating.

Let's look at the case of Mary Beth Briscoe, who worked as the chief financial officer at the UAB (University of Alabama at Birmingham) School of Medicine. Mary Beth was a world-class leader with numerous degrees. As

CFO, Mary Beth was responsible for a multi-billion-dollar budget, along with all the stresses and strains involved with high-level fiscal management.

Make no mistake about it—Mary Beth loved her work. But one day, when I happened to talk with her after an excessively stressful day for her, she was weighed down with misgivings from deadlines and various pressures. As busy as she was, I urged her to schedule an hour with me in thoracic surgery. Reluctantly, the next day, she stopped in to watch an operation and then joined me in talking with the families of two patients. One of those cases had gone very well. Mary Beth delighted in sharing their relief and happiness.

The news for the next family was bleak. When we first placed our scope in the chest, we found many metastatic deposits of cancer on the patient's chest wall. The patient's cancer had spread widely. The CAT scan and other forms of imaging we'd done prior to surgery did not and could not have seen these multiple small lesions. Mary Beth opened her heart to this family, too, offering comfort and sharing their worries and tears as we broke the news to them of this devastating finding.

Despite the emotional mixed bag, she told me later, "This is one of the fullest days I've had in ten years." The experience helped Mary Beth remember just one reason she loves what she does, which restored meaning and motivation to her daily life. Getting swept up in the wave of budgets and dollar signs, she may have partially forgotten the people behind all the numbers and the great work she did every day. The spreadsheets represented thousands of doctors, nurses, and other hospital staff, as well as all the patients fighting for their lives against illness and injury. She may not have been the one to use the scalpel, but Mary Beth personally helped those people by doing a superb job at financial management.

Keep Life in Perspective

Mary Beth's story leads to another strategy for maintaining your passion for work: effectively managing the highs and lows. If you were living in fantasyland, all the low points would disappear with the swipe of a wand. In the real world, it's a package deal. There's not much we can guarantee in life, but I can give you a foolproof guarantee that you're going to have ups and downs—glorious successes and devastating losses ride the ebbs and the flows.

You can live reactively, spinning out of control with glee or despair as each new triumph or defeat comes your way. Or you can commit to staying on an even keel as best you are able. Welcome your victories with humility. Have respect and gratitude for all the others who contributed to the effort. Avoid the booby traps of smugness, conceit, hubris, arrogance, or overconfidence, all of which are likely to make your stay on the mountaintop a brief one. And don't forget to review your work and continue to look for ways to improve.

Humility is needed on the down side, too, in part to help you keep the lows in perspective and prevent you from catastrophizing. Accepting losses is a skill you can acquire—taking your failures with grace and accountability. Rather than lashing out in all directions with blame or judgment, acknowledge your mistakes candidly and be prepared to take measures to avoid repeat disasters. Notice whether you're feeling shame or guilt and do your utmost to let go of such destructive emotions. A person whose mind is cluttered with negativity and denial has a high likelihood of getting stuck rehashing the problem over and over again. They may lose the resilience needed to recover from a bad situation. That's a form of self-sabotage, which makes things worse by adding insult to injury.

Even if you've suffered a terrible setback, make a commitment to stay engaged and get back in the game instead of giving up or quitting. In the O.R., the stakes are so high that a loss can cause severe demoralization. Two years ago, a surgical resident worked with our team on a beautiful young girl. Although the operation went fine, the girl had a co-existing disease that took her life. The devastated resident was ready to throw in the towel and get out of surgery. I've been in those shoes. So, I can tell you that pushing away the pain of loss doesn't fix anything.

You will suffer losses, failures, and embarrassments in

your life. Keep the faith, stay committed, work hard, and continue to engage open-heartedly with your colleagues. This attitude or philosophy will greatly improve your odds of making it past the low spots. On the other hand, if you flee the low points, you will not experience the high ones and they will not taste as sweet. You have to go through, not around. Nor will you be able to cultivate the passion for your work that will spur you on to great leadership and create meaning and value in your life.

Ask Yourself, "What's My Calling?"

My father was a surgeon, and when I was thirteen, he decided that the safest and most effective way to spay our beloved beagle, Spot, would be for him to do it himself at home, in our basement. He even did his own anesthesia. He allowed me to be a surgical assistant during the hysterectomy. The surgery went beautifully, and Spot was her sparky, thriving self again in no time. Spot was still Spot, but I was changed. I'd found my calling. Having grown up with a family ethic of hard work, drive, service, and achievement, I had the right combination of role models, personality, and circumstance to make my dream a reality.

Today, I am as deeply passionate about my work as ever, maybe even more so, especially teaching. I love performing surgery; I love teaching; I love being a leader and learning how to lead better; I love lecturing about surgery and work/life balance; and I love the private coaching I do for other surgeons. A few years back, I went back to grad school for my MBA, and I love working with the business intelligence group and the operating room efficiency at my hospital. I also love my life out of the hospital—my passion is exercising, especially in the sun. I received my personal training degree in order to learn to work out better and more efficiently. Many of you reading this book have similar passions and pursuits of excellence. We should pursue excellence in all parts of our life.

The many long, long days and hard hours we put in are worth it because of the passion we have for our work, but it would be sugarcoating things deceptively to ignore the realities of the working world. You may find yourself in a position where you dislike your job or your company, or its management, culture, internal politics, mission, or values. Frankly speaking, if you are working at a job that conflicts with your fundamental values and personality, you will ultimately need to find a new position where you can work and live more authentically. You simply won't be able to love what you do, be a great leader, or find happiness on the job. For now, though, it may be in your family's best interest for you to stay put. That doesn't prohibit you from making long-term plans to attain a more suitable career match. Focusing on the longer term may even alleviate your present travails.

Meanwhile, whether you're in it for the short or long

term, you can influence your situation for the better. Start with a candid assessment of your own attitude, opting for a more positive approach and creating more positive energy around yourself. This may demand letting go of some habits that have become all too comfortable. Are you participating in gossip, trash talk, or endless complaining and criticizing? Have you gotten caught in a negative feedback loop? Are resentment and feelings of being cheated or victimized making you unproductive and unable to do your best work?

Take a long look to see whether these kinds of behaviors reflect who you are and what you believe. You can be who you want to be, as long as your aspirations and values are consistently aligned. You must be sincerely willing to change and to substitute positive behaviors that will be kinder and less toxic to you and your co-workers.

Shifting attitude gears is remarkably simple. It only takes the desire to do it and the discipline to persist. Then you just stop saying and doing those things that cause harm. The benefits will start appearing quickly, even if it's only a loosening of that knot in your stomach at the end of the day. What muddies the water here is your own mind as it subtly resists change, setting up straw men and empty rationalizations. Be true to yourself and you can gradually rewire your brain with habits that emerge from positive, authentic behaviors.

Changing your mindset will have a big impact in reducing feelings of being trapped and powerless. Next, look for changes you can make without resigning. Maybe you can transfer jobs or find a way to do something you love in a different part of the company. Consider shifting your schedule to better suit your needs. With your head clear of these conflicts, identify parts of your job or workday that you do enjoy. Then direct and redirect your attention to them. When you slip up or have a setback, don't sweat it. Just start over again.

Take advantage of any opportunities for mastery. Is there training available or a chance to learn new software, skills, or techniques? That's a way to increase your value to your current employer while enhancing your resume for a potential future job change. It's also an effective method of distracting yourself from the things that make you miserable.

Take time to appreciate any rewards of your job. Maybe it's close to home, you have health insurance, a regular paycheck, or you're able to feed your family. Maybe there are some people you work with whom you like and respect. Perhaps the organization—even if it's unhealthy—produces goods or services that help people live better lives. These things may seem trivial, but, on balance, they can reduce the daily stressors that eat away at your well-being. You can also try putting more energy into areas of your life outside of work, such as your kids, home, church, hobbies, or social activities.

Dig down to find the good within the bad. Recently, we were having a challenging day in the O.R. Despite our best efforts, we had a few bad operations, difficult procedures, and a number of delays—definitely a subpar day. In the short break between our eighth and ninth cases, I happened to turn on my cellphone and answer a call. At another hospital, a surgeon had operated on a man's esophagus. Now three days post-operatively, the patient's esophagus was leaking infected material in his chest and part of his stomach was dying.

We could have said no to the transfer. It was a rough day and we were behind. I had a meeting scheduled for 4:30 that afternoon. Nevertheless, we knew our team could help this man. I gave instructions to keep him intubated, put him in an ambulance, and quickly send him over to us. It all worked. We repaired the problems and he did well. We chose to direct our attention to a good part of the day rather than to obsess over things that went wrong.

None of these strategies is going to fix a dysfunctional work environment that's damaged beyond hope. However, taking steps such as improving your attitude, dropping negative behaviors, mastering new skills, and appreciating the good things will make a bad job easier to bear. On top of that, if and when the time comes to move on, the "new you" will possess enhanced skills, capabilities, and mental qualities that will make you eminently desirable to new employers.

Be Aware of Burnout Symptoms

It's surprisingly easy to conflate the experience of burnout with hating your job because burnout often masquerades as job dissatisfaction. The two are similar, but not identical, and it may be helpful for you to figure out which one you're experiencing. Physicians, nurses, first responders, bankers, and teachers are among the jobs with higher levels of burnout, but in today's world, the phenomenon is widespread across many occupations.

People suffering from burnout display a variety of stress-induced symptoms, such as exhaustion, lack of energy and motivation, inability to concentrate, loss of productivity, negativity, feeling overwhelmed, insomnia, changes in appetite, anger, anxiety, et cetera. Causes of burnout may include long hours, insufficient rewards and recognition, feeling powerless, a dysfunctional workplace, lack of peer support, or simply not feeling valued. Burnout can also result from the situation I mentioned earlier, where there's a misalignment between your core values and those of your organization.

This book is about leadership, not occupational stress or improving your working conditions. However, as we examine the relationship between great leadership and loving what you do, it's obvious that burnout is a major barrier to cultivating both your passion and your leadership skills. Take some time to reflect on whether the symptoms and causes of burnout are impacting your life.

If you decide that burnout is a factor, you may want to prioritize the problem and focus on developing coping strategies that help you overcome it.

Chances are that an "if-only" approach—if only I had a better title, more money, more power, higher sales, etc.—isn't going to eliminate burnout. Extensive resources and support are available to help you assess what kinds of behavioral, lifestyle, and occupational changes you can implement to alleviate burnout. Once you've untangled those issues, you'll have a clearer path to rediscovering your passion and becoming a great leader.

Actively and Frequently Retool Your Plans for Happiness

Happiness matters. It matters to all of us, whether we realize it or not. One way or another, everyone is seeking happiness. Paradoxically, many people seek happiness in ways that have the exact opposite effect, causing harm, pain, and suffering. That's because we humans often confuse the pursuit of happiness with hedonism—the individual's pursuit of pleasure and self-gratification. Happiness, meanwhile, involves contentment, joy, and well-being, along with the feeling that your life is worthwhile, meaningful, and purposeful.

Essential happiness is good for you and those around you. Time and again, researchers study happiness and find a string of beneficial side effects. Compared to unhappy folks, happy people tend to have longer lives, better health, stronger immunity to disease, greater resilience, happier marriages, more friends, better coping skills, lower stress, greater satisfaction with their lives, more money, higher productivity, and greater community involvement.

That's why happiness is worth cultivating and protecting. Many of us meet with a financial adviser yearly or even quarterly to redirect our financial strategies, but few of us meet with our families to retool our happiness strategies. Write down your happiness strategies, including the things that make you happy and the ways in which you plan to pursue happiness. You should re-evaluate your happiness plan every three or four months, just the way you'd update your budget or your investment plan.

Practicing kindness, compassion, altruism, love, faith, gratitude, generosity, and respect will inherently improve your happiness levels. So, will material contributions of your time, skills, goods, or money to charitable organizations and in service to others.

Loving what you do will bring you happiness. And happy people are more inclined to love what they do. Truly great leaders are not only happy themselves; they also make others happy. How? Great leaders inspire others to be the best they can be. They motivate others to contribute their best work to a group outcome that exceeds what any one individual might achieve. As it turns out, one of the best markers for happiness is the degree to which you can make other people happy. By inspiring and motivating team members to be their best selves, great leaders are helping those people find self-worth, meaning, and happiness.

Allow Evolution in Your Job—Reinvent Yourself Every Seven Years

Many of us have been at the same job or similar job for a long time. Although we may like what we do, after a while it becomes work. What's more, few of us are able to completely start a new job in mid-career because of the needs of our families and others dependent on us. Therefore, it makes sense, even if you love your job, to start thinking about your next iteration of your existing job. Most occupations can be twisted—meaning you can talk with your leadership, tell them your eventual interests, and start a pathway to keep your old job in the same company or business, but find a new avenue that interests you. I have done this with my MBA and administrative works. I still love operating more than any other work I do, but I know it is a young man's game that at some point I will eventually have to stop for my patients' best interest as my physical skills and/or dexterity at some point erode over time, like any professional athlete.

Chapter 3

Leadership Starts with an "I"

You read the chapter title, "Leadership Starts with an 'I,'" and in the back of your head you say, "That can't be right." It is, instead, a chance to adopt a new way of understanding yourself in conjunction with developing your personal leadership potential. I know some who literally count the number of times the word "I" is used in another person's speech to assess their leadership. I can teach anyone to say "we" instead of "I," but that artificial, blemish-hiding cream will not change their culture or their intrinsic ability to lead better. I can go through this entire book and change every "I" to "we," and that may change the narrative and make it sound more like a "really good book on leadership," but it does not make me a better leader.

Leadership is much more than substituting "we" over "I" in your speech or writings, but it is about substituting "we" over "I" in your culture and thoughts.

In some regards, though, yes, leadership begins with an "I." You can think of it as the "I" in identity—your leadership identity. To become a successful leader, you need to turn your gaze inward and focus on your beliefs, values, mindsets, actions, and behaviors. Learn to nurture the personal characteristics that will strengthen your sense of identity and your ability to lead others with heart, vision, and competence. Without those qualities, you will never be an exceptional leader because people will not trust, cooperate with, or be inspired or motivated by you. People will not follow you unless you offer something better than another to follow. You must first build a platform—an actualized you—from which to lead. That is part of the "I" in leadership to which this chapter refers. You cannot lead if you first are not accomplished.

To be an effective leader, you must possess the drive to lead, a high level of competence, and knowledge of how to make and delegate decisions in the best interest of the group. This part of leadership works from the inside out, and while you can't fake it, you can learn it. You can bolster your leadership identity by building at least some of the traits and inner skills associated with it. Strong leaders are generally considered to be charismatic, decisive, forceful, assured, capable, creative, goal-oriented, and authoritative.

Don't confuse that last one—authoritative—with authoritarian. Leaders who are authoritative know the ropes.

They may earn the trust and respect of their colleagues due to their command of the subject matter and their expertise in workplace structure and operations. Authoritativeness is a quality of a good leader, while authoritarian is a leadership style by which a leader exercises power. Authoritarian leaders tend to call all the shots, directing and controlling their subordinates' activities with little or no input or feedback. This form of leadership style is commonly ineffective in today's culture.

Walking the Tightrope

We'll delve more into leadership styles later in the book, but the concept of authoritarian leadership is relevant here, as we consider the "I" in leadership. It represents a kind of leadership tightrope that you must learn how to walk, well balanced, lest you take a bruising fall onto the pavement. Such a hard fall can hurt you personally and professionally, and it may cause serious damage in your workplace, too. Think of this as a balancing act between "I" and "we—between your leadership identity as an individual and the good of the team and its work.

One aspect of that balancing act is understanding the seductive nature of power. However you came to be a leader, whether or not you have an official leadership title, the very act of leading involves a hands-on use of power. Being a leader feels good. People look up to you, turn to you for guidance and wisdom. They expect you'll always know the right course of action. Successes make you hungry for more. Your wins trigger a feeling of headiness—which is just a step or two shy of hubris. There's an invisible line between striving to be a great leader by doing great work and seeking more power for its own sake.

We surgeons spend years—decades—competing and winning. In high school, we pushed for top grades to attend the best colleges. We drove ourselves in college because we knew only the cream of the crop get into medical school. Many of us played sports, captained teams, and achieved superlatives in other areas. After medical school, we did our stints as interns, residents, and fellows. Two-thirds of general surgery residents used to burn out before the end of the five-year program, and about a fifth drop out entirely. Most surgeons are in their early thirties before they're fully certified to do an operation alone, much less head up other surgeons.

So here you are as a surgeon, age 32, your head packed with the latest medical knowledge and research, your hands skilled in the optimal techniques and technology. You've run the gauntlet, endured, worked inconceivably hard, and come out on top. You're self-assured, confident in your talent and technical proficiency. You know how to give orders and demand what you need at the operating table. You're drilled in responding to emergencies. You feel ready to take the reins in the O.R., start saving lives, and maybe rake in some glory and big bucks in the process. Full speed ahead, right?

Wrong. We've been competing so long that as we move into the surgical arena, we sometimes face a drive to keep competing, to measure our success by how well we beat out others and stand out above the crowd. We were the kid in the sandbox who took all the toys and wouldn't share. In the O.R., surgeons are members of a team whose work is undermined by leaders who demonstrate that kind of sandbox mentality, even if only at a very subtle level. It may feel like you're king of the hill, but it's actually evidence of a lack of leadership.

Although the surgeon's situation in the O.R. is a stark example of the balance between the "I" and "we" of leadership, it applies anywhere, whether you're a software engineer or assistant manager of a fast-food restaurant. Expertise—and confidence in that expertise—are not enough to maintain your balance and make you a great leader. To do that, you will need to foster the qualities that strengthen both the "I" of your leadership identity and the "we" of your identity as a member of a team.

Changing Perspective from "I" to "We"

To excel as a leader, you're always going to need some degree of what we call ego: enough faith in yourself and your abilities to assert your ideas and persuade others to follow your direction. At some point, though, you may start to incline toward a kind of leadership that is more expansive and more inclusive than the "I alone" model. You may begin to fully appreciate that **leadership is taking a team concept and turning it into a team outcome.** And that your role as a great leader is to **inspire and engage your team members to embrace an idea—either yours or someone else's that is better—and work hard together to make it a reality.**

To be honest, I wasn't doing that during my first few years out of training. The last thing I wanted to hear in my O.R. was that another doctor did something differently. I wasn't secure enough in my abilities to entertain many ideas outside what I believed to be true. Many years ago, with just a couple years in the O.R., I recall snapping at a team member, "Listen, I don't care what the hell Dr. X does, this is my O.R. and my patient and this is how I do it!" It's a little embarrassing to admit today, but the reality is that I was very green, immature, and had much to learn.

I'm still learning, although my learning curve isn't quite as steep. My mind is more open to the new and more tolerant of the unknown. As the scope of my work has expanded to include robotics, teaching, coaching and training surgeons all over the world, and business management, I find myself embracing the "we" aspect of leadership. It has helped me be better at my jobs and be a happier person—and that's why I'm sharing it here.

You may see this transition as a kind of softening—something undesirable in a surgeon whose job demands a militaristic precision in the ability to take command and make split-second, critical decisions. But just the opposite is true. Leaders with too much self-importance and need for control waste energy defending their mental turf and fighting off perceived threats. That keeps new and improved ideas and practices from entering the system. Alternatively, a leader with a flexible, open mind is quicker to learn and quicker to facilitate changes that improve functions, processes, and outcomes.

Our surgical team works in an academic environment known as a teaching hospital. Medical students routinely observe and scrub into our operations. We also have surgeons from around the country and the world observing, either in person or via live video. A few years ago, we were finishing up a surgery and I was starting to close up the chest when a medical student asked, "Are you going to put a chest tube in?" In lung surgery, before closing, we insert a tube in the chest to draw out any small amounts of blood or fluid.

Though we rarely make this kind of oversight, I had indeed forgotten the chest tube! The student had spoken out in time to make a difference, allowing me to place the tube. Afterwards, I told him, "It's great that you told me. I give you so much credit for not being intimated and speaking up!" The student replied, "Well, Dr. Cerfolio, you maintain an atmosphere where you let everyone talk and give an opinion. If this were my neurosurgical rotation, I wouldn't have said a word in fear they'd have yelled at me to shut up."

In our O.R., we don't think medical students should be seen and not heard. We try to create an ambiance where people can safely voice their questions and comments. It's occasionally annoying when too many trivial questions arise, but most of the time, people are respectful. In a few cases, they've come up with ingenious ideas and new perspectives that have improved our surgical processes or the way we teach. By building inclusion and avenues for greater input right into our system, our team improves, our results improve, our students learn more, and our work environment is healthier. That's the power of the "we."

I now view everyone who comes into our operating room as a potential fountain of information from others outside our silo. Surgeons may be the most siloed of all doctors, working 10 to 12 hours a day, concentrating on a small area of the body, and watching only our ourselves perform. We all think we are much better than average, but the reality is half of us have to be less than average. Every visitor—and we have had over twelve hundred come to watch our team perform—brings knowledge of a different way to do things, and perhaps a better culture and way. The inexperienced do not wear the biases lens of a lifetime of habits, some of which probably could be changed for the better, and the experienced from other countries offer new and refreshing ways of doing things. If we create an atmosphere where they all are willing to talk, teach, and express their observations and opinions, as well as be taught, we all win.

How to Lead from within the Team

Remember, you're maintaining a balance here between the "I" of your ego and the "we" of the team. Don't lose the positive aspects of your individual leadership identity as you cultivate the characteristics that will increase your sense of partnership and collaborative efforts on a team. Here are some methods of improving your collaborative skills and help make your team a "we" team.

- **Become a better listener and communicator.** Learn to articulate your thoughts clearly and notice how well they are received. If you aren't communicating well, find a new way to express yourself, rather than just repeating the same thing the same way, over and over. Practice active listening, which means you focus full attention on the person who's speaking, instead of what's going on inside your head.
- **Become more trustworthy** by acting in ways that merit the trust of your coworkers, managers, subordinates, and clients. When people trust you, they will support you in your leadership role. Always be aware of and true to your core values and the role they play in your work life.
- As a leader, **learn to create a safe space for people to speak out, take risks, and make mistakes.**

- **Make sure to be honest and accountable about your own mistakes.**
- **Know your weaknesses, as well as your strengths.** Welcome the kind of input from others, however difficult to hear, that will give you greater self-knowledge, understanding, and confidence in your leadership decisions.
- **Consider doing a 360-degree evaluation of those above you, below you, and at the same level as you, and make changes based on the results.** This takes confidence, courage, and thick skin, but it can really help you understand your effectiveness as a leader. A 360-degree assessment allows all the people around you to provide anonymous feedback about your job performance and behaviors. The evaluators are your superiors, peers, and subordinates, and may also include clients, patients, students, customers, or other stakeholders in your work.

Humility versus Hubris

Let's face it, doctors have something of a reputation for arrogance and a lack of humility. But it's not just doctors. These days, when we have so much information available to us instantaneously, it's all too easy to have the surety and self-righteousness of a Monday-morning quarterback. We see the mistakes others have made and we think we could do better. Sadly, the need or desire to be right all the time can be incredibly destructive, both personally and in the workplace. It's one of the main components of hubris.

Now, we've already discussed that in order to be a great leader, you absolutely must have some of the qualities connected to what is sometimes called a healthy ego, such as confidence and authority. Remember: this is a balancing act between the individual traits required to maintain a leadership role and those that support the effective functions of the group. It's not a contest between humility and hubris, and this isn't a matter of choosing between the "I" and "we" of leadership. Rather, you have to learn to balance them and to do so on an ongoing basis, because personality changes usually don't happen overnight. Being humble doesn't involve acting overly self-effacing or putting yourself down all the time. Humility means you respect the value of other people. At the same time, humility includes acknowledging—but not overinflating—your own self-worth. You can be a strong, confident, and effective leader, and also be a supportive team member.

Samuel Tilden was a former governor of New York who ran for the U.S. presidency on the Democratic ticket in 1876. When the votes were tallied, Tilden had more than fifty percent of the popular vote and led in the Electoral College by a single vote. Sadly, for Tilden, twenty electoral votes from four states remained in dispute. He was ahead in the Electoral College but didn't have enough votes to win. Manual counting was a tedious and unreliable process in those days, and the controversy over who actually won the four states was never resolved.

When the dust settled months later, an appointed commission brokered a deal that gave the Democrats some major concessions that would increase the party's power in the South. The contested votes, however, were allocated to the Republican candidate, Rutherford B. Hayes, who went on to become the nineteenth president, with a one-vote margin in the Electoral College and a minority of the popular vote. Tilden is the only candidate in American history to win a majority of the popular vote without winning the presidency at that time. He had some valuable reflections on leadership:

"It is said that it is far more difficult to hold and maintain leadership (liberty) than it is to attain it. Success is a ruthless competitor for it flatters and nourishes our weaknesses and lulls us into complacency. We bask in the sunshine of accomplishment and lose the spirit of humility which helps us visualize all the factors which have contributed to our success. We are apt to forget that we are only one of a team, that in unity there is strength, and that we are strong only as long as each unit in our organization functions with precision."

Chapter 4

Why Do You Want to Lead, Anyway?

Really, who wouldn't want the prestige, profits, power, and perks that come with leadership? Glowing images of leadership, success, and celebrity are so imprinted in this country's psyche that it's automatically assumed we all want to move up the ladder and that leaders stand atop the ladder of success. Everyone wants to run the show and reap the benefits that come with the VIP package, right?

Not always. Many people actually don't want the responsibilities and spotlight that often accompany a position of leadership. They want to do their jobs, earn their paychecks, and come home to focus on their families, hobbies, social activities, or other priorities. That is perfectly acceptable. Yet people who back away from the sometimes-fierce competition in the race to the top are often disparaged as lacking ambition, lazy, or foolish.

Thomas Merton was a twentieth-century Trappist monk who was a scholar, deep thinker, poet, and prolific writer. On the subject of life's pursuits, he wrote: "People may spend their whole lives climbing the ladder of success only to find, once they reach the top, that the ladder is leaning against the wrong wall."

This is your chance for a kind of gut check—to decide whether you sincerely want to pursue leadership in your work and elsewhere in your life. It's a time for you to explore and evaluate your motives, to take a look at how your material goals stack up against your inner ambitions and heart's desires. This is the opportunity to choose the right wall for your ladder.

Mixed-up Motives

First and foremost, **why do you want to be a leader?** That's absolutely the single-most important question in determining a career path or deciding to apply for an open position in management. Be brutally honest about it now and you'll thank yourself later. Are you seduced by the image of your name on a door with a fancy title underneath? Maybe you're thinking about the reserved parking spot or all the bills you can pay off due to the extra digits on a fatter paycheck? Do you look forward to having power over a co-worker who treated you poorly in the past?

Unfortunately, if it's all about the glamour, power, or money, it's not likely to work out very well for you. Motives that are strictly materialistic do not result in long-term happiness or satisfaction. You may get swept up in seeking ever more glamor, power, or money while the deeper desire to do meaningful work goes unfulfilled. What's more, those kinds of motivations are big distractions that can impede your ability to be effective on the job and lead to failure. Drive and ambition are great assets. Excessive greed and blind ambition mean trouble.

Self-exploration and self-awareness will help you open up the hood, get a good look at your own engine, and help you assess your true motivations—which may not be simple to untangle. We all have mixed motives, multiple motives. That's human nature. To be both happy and successful in leadership, you need to candidly evaluate whether your main motives are more than just material ones.

It's completely legitimate to incorporate your desire for the material perks and benefits into your evaluation process. Don't condemn yourself for having those feelings, but at the same time, don't let them override another critical question about why you want to lead. Do you support your company's mission and possess the genuine desire and ability to contribute toward its success? Unless you can answer this affirmatively, you are probably bound for a significant amount of internal and external conflict if you take on this leadership position.

Now, About the Money

This is absolutely not to suggest you should put yourself on some kind of idealistic pedestal of purity. As Madonna sang, "We are living in a material world." As you're contemplating a move to leadership, it's normal and healthy to want to maximize your income. I endorse those efforts entirely—as long as you factor in all the true costs, including the hidden costs. None aspire to climb down the financial ladder.

What price will you pay for a high-profile leadership position that requires you to compromise your beliefs and values? Let's say you're a nurse or a doctor in a medical system that doesn't share your personal beliefs on abortion. It's one thing to be part of that organization doing the daily good work of caring for your patients. It's something else to be in a top leadership position where your work would involve promoting views that contradict your core values.

Perhaps you work at a company that makes a high-quality product or service, and you're generally proud to be part of the team. Yet the company overcharges or engages in unethical business or manufacturing practices or treats its employees poorly. How comfortable would you be as a member of that company's leadership tier? Perhaps you're the person who can bring about positive change in that regard. That's definitely a valid motive for taking the job, assuming you're being realistic about your chances of effecting those changes.

This is not complicated, especially if you're proactive with your decision-making. Keep it simple and forego the rationalizations and justifications. You can't compromise your values to take a leadership role just because it pays more money. Nor can you compromise your underlying beliefs and the kind of person you are inside. Don't take such a job. There are other ways to get a fatter paycheck. Doors open for people who act with integrity and the courage of their convictions.

Trade-offs

After you figure out why you want to be a leader, the next thing to ask yourself is what you're willing to give up in the end. People often underestimate how much a new position entails. In the hospital, for example, a surgeon who moves into management will probably spend less time in the O.R., scalpel in hand. That is what most of us enjoy the most, the challenge of the operating room and the instant gratification of smiles and hugs from patients and families after surgery.

By the way, leadership doesn't always translate to more money. A tax attorney, for instance, who's moving from the private sector to run for elected office may be in for a big pay cut. People who get paid a piece rate or project rate and those who are eligible for overtime pay may take a hit moving into a salaried, exempt management job.

Numerous other trade-offs may exist for you—things you have to sacrifice to do a good job for the benefit of the team. These might include less time with your family, less travel, less leisure time, more internal politics, more backbiting and competition, more bureaucracy, and you may be subject to frequent criticism and gossip.

You may decide that the trade-offs involved are well worth it, and maybe you'll be able to devise ways that you can mitigate them in the short or long term. However, it's essential to fully comprehend what you're getting into on the front end so that you can make an informed choice. Once you're down the rabbit hole, you won't find it easy to get back to where you were.

Other Questions

No doubt you've heard the slogan "Question Authority." Well, in this case, it's "Question Yourself." Before you sit down to decide about leadership, make yourself a list of questions to contemplate. They will vary with your situation, of course, but here are some examples:

- What are the negatives that come with the new position?
- What types of skills will you need to perform well in the new role?
- Which of these skills do you have already, and which would you need to acquire?
- Are you capable of learning new skills on the

job or will you have to do outside studying and training?

- What are the company's expectations of you and your performance? Are they realistic?
- Given the nature of the organization, how long will it take for you to start seeing progress on your goals and management's expectations?
- Are you risk averse? Is the organization risk averse? Are you being hired to change a culture that you can't?
- Does the position require instant decisions and bold action? Do you have to make enemies and/or fire people in order to effect change? How does that sync up with your personality? Some people are inclined to move more slowly and deliberately. Having to act in a way that's counter to your true nature may make you miserable.
- Who are the people with whom you'll be working most closely? Do you like them, respect them, and get along with them?
- Do you have the patience and stamina to deal with difficult people and complex situations?
- What's the real-world time commitment? How will it affect your outside life?
- When you envision yourself in your new leadership role, how does it feel?

- How well do you tolerate constructive and negative criticism? Is your skin too thin for the job, and if so, is thicker skin something you think you can acquire?
- Are you capable of acknowledging mistakes and learning from failure?
- How well do you juggle priorities, switch gears, and manage your time?
- Will you be happier with the new job?

Time and Timing

Keep an open mind in evaluating your potential move. Take the time for a well-rounded analysis that includes the various pros and cons we've been discussing and your ability to perform the job at the standards of quality and personal values that mean the most to you. You don't want to agonize endlessly and indecisively over every minute detail. However, you do want to take as much time as the situation allows to think things through with a calm, clear, and rational approach. Be aware that too much external pressure to make a quick decision may indicate that something is amiss. Good leadership is vital to success for any organization and they should support a careful decision-making process on your part.

As with all things in life, leadership opportunities will come and go. When your chance to lead arises, consider the timing. Is it right for you, in terms of your skills and other circumstances in your life? If you don't seize the day now, will this or a similar opportunity still be there for you in a year or two or five? Timing is the most intangible of all the questions in your deliberation process, but it is no less significant. You may find it helpful to ask a trusted friend or relative to help you sift through the issues to reach a viable resolution.

Applying Leadership and Vision Without the Title

You can decline to pursue a formal leadership title and still be a leader. Opportunities for you to practice, grow, and cultivate vision exist in every aspect of your life. You can exhibit leadership at your work, in your family, in your daily tasks and activities, with your friends, and in all the human interactions that fill your day-to-day life.

Yes, that even includes those times when you have to deal with Customer Service at the cable company or talk to someone in an overseas call center for tech support on your computer. Admittedly, you may not fully resolve the problem with your cable bill, but you can use the opportunity to improve your leadership skills and apply them in ways that makes you more effective and, frankly, less vulnerable to everyday stresses.

This works in two ways. First, recall that outstanding leaders inspire and engage their team members to embrace a vision and work hard to make it a reality. They inspire others to be the absolute best they can be as they work toward common goals. We're not talking about manipulating someone to get your way. That tech support guy is a human being trying to earn a living and do the best job he can. Maintain the assumption that you're on the same team whose goal is resolving your problem—and treat him accordingly. Inspire him to embrace that idea and to do his best in working toward the mutual goal. Thank him sincerely for his help.

Second, consider the personal qualities that a great leader needs, such as clear communications, authenticity, humility, positivity, and trustworthiness. Find the ones that resonate most with you, sharpen those skills, and allow yourself to fully incorporate them into your belief system. Let these leadership traits guide you toward being more responsive and less reactive in your daily interactions.

Again, no guarantee that these skills are going to deliver a magic-fix outcome to your troubles. In fact, difficulties are among the few things in the world that are sure to arise sometimes. When you finally hang up the phone with tech support, you may still have that frustrating Blue Screen of Death forcing you to haul your laptop into a data recovery shop, but you'll find it much easier to bear when you've acted with the integrity connected to the qualities of great leadership.

It's certain you'll have your share of trials and tribulations but learning to blend your core values into your thoughts, words, and actions will make you more successful and happy in all aspects of your life. You're strengthening your leadership muscles, with the bonus of the happiness, meaning, and fulfillment that come from improving the alignment of your lifestyle with your values. Whether you have that parking space or not, those are great benefits of honing your leadership skills.

CHAPTER 5

THREE THINGS YOU NEED TO DO

In the world of property and real estate, they say the three most important factors are location, location, location. In youth sports, coaches teach little kids the three things they need to do to become good players and a great team: practice; practice; directed, efficient practice.

In leadership lingo, we can translate this to the three things you need to do to build a successful team and be an effective leader. Since we're talking in threes, there are three ways in which practice is key to great leadership.

First, leaders teach their team members how to practice the skills and habits they need for individual and collective success. The closer practice simulates the game, the better, because we practice the way we play. Second, leaders build the culture of practice into the team's operational structure. Third, leadership is not innate; it can be taught, which means it's something you can practice.

That's right—leaders learn how to lead, and they practice the skills and mental habits needed to lead.

Many people mistakenly believe that leadership comes naturally—either you've got what it takes, or you don't. There's a widespread misconception that these "born leaders" are charismatic extroverts, with an almost magical ability to inspire others and create positive outcomes. In reality, you could be the most charismatic person on the planet and still not have one whit of leadership ability.

Or you could be a soft-spoken introvert and grow into a competent and visionary leader. Take sixteenth President Abraham Lincoln. Born in a primitive log cabin in Kentucky, his family lived a backwoods, pioneering lifestyle. Lincoln was hardly the kind of child you'd expect to grow up to lead America through its greatest existential crisis, the Civil War. His father was a farmer, but as a young boy, Lincoln developed a passion for books and learning, spending his nights quietly reading by firelight.

Almost entirely self-educated, Lincoln became an attorney and a state lawmaker in Illinois before winning the presidency in 1860. He was a great listener—a consensus builder. However, Lincoln was not a born leader. He learned and practiced the skills he needed to lead the country as it ended slavery and survived a bloody, divisive war.

What "Practice" Means in the O.R.

Turn to any dictionary and you'll read multiple definitions of "practice." There's the "practice" of medicine, which is different in meaning from the "practice" you do in order to learn and improve at something, involving repetition, training, and drilling. Patients in the O.R. can be reassured that surgical practice does not fall into the latter category. All the techniques, instruments, equipment, drugs, supplies, and communications we use are tested and evaluated for maximum clinical safety before they're put in service anywhere near the operating room. Even so-called experimental treatments that we might use in extreme, last-resort cases have undergone rigorous study and testing.

Surgeons clearly know the difference between the meanings of practice. Around the operating table, our team is not practicing; we're executing the byproduct of more than 10,000 hours of practice—at the highest level of expertise available. Then how do we learn and improve? How do we respond most skillfully to an unexpected emergency? With a lot of review, analysis, and attention to detail, and then more directed practice to specific areas that need to be improved.

- We continue our education and stay abreast of scientific literature and developments.
- We review and analyze the videotapes of our operations and documentation of our work and that of others.
- We evaluate our mistakes at monthly conferences in order to get better.

- We use root-cause analysis to help identify the parts of the process that might be responsible.

We practice, too, just the way you might practice piano, but we do it both inside the operating room and out. Surgical teams use tried-and-true methods of practice, where we repeatedly drill our responses and our mental states for when things go south. We practice as teams, we use team huddles and team time-outs to review almost every conceivable scenario and our response to them. And we do this every day and review videotapes of our operations most every day.

We use team-building events to positively foster work relationships that further enhance our ability to work through and solve critical problems. All of this is done to maximize our patients' outcomes. In addition, the latest technological advances have brought us a wonderful new array of options for practice that simply didn't exist ten or twenty years ago. Numerous types of surgical simulation software—many of which employ virtual reality—are available to replicate nearly every aspect of the surgical environment for the purposes of learning and practice. There are now robotic-procedure specific operations we can use to hone our skills in very specific ways. Even our robotic hands' movements can be traced, measured and assessed for efficiency and accuracy.

With and without simulators, surgical teams practice for every possible contingency: natural disasters, fires in the O.R., and what to do in an electrical blackout. We run drills to respond rapidly and effectively to things that may go wrong during surgery. Every member of the team has practiced and memorized the emergency response choreography. The repetition prevents panic and facilitates quick action when the real-life emergency inevitably occurs. In some ways, it turns the exceptional into the routine. Just like an athlete that relies on his or her routine before a critical part of the game to help them perform, we do the same.

Our team was recently in the midst of a robotic operation when we were thrown into crisis. Robotic lung surgery is minimally invasive, meaning the instruments and the incisions used are very small in order to reduce post-operative pain and speed recovery. The disadvantage is that if you put a hole in a major artery or vein, massive hemorrhage can occur, and you do not have your hands in the chest or abdomen to quickly stop it.

Until that point, the procedure had gone beautifully. Suddenly, we had a major hole in the pulmonary artery with rapid bleeding. Seamlessly, our team shifted into the crisis mode for which we've trained so extensively. Our emergency protocols took over almost naturally and a deliberate step-by-step process was launched. We employed the "Four P's" that I have lectured to other teams about all over the world:

- **Poise**: You must not convey panic to your team, or their performance will suffer.

- **Pressure:** It is best to place direct pressure on the bleeding artery and avoid the reflexive action of grappling it or compressing it.
- **Proximal control:** Obtain control of the vessel in front of where the hole is.
- **Preparedness**: Allow your team's practice and preparation for this moment to take over. Relax—stayed poised—and let your training and your practice to direct your actions.

And many surgeons add a fifth P:

- **Prayers.**

Two or three steps into our process, we were still unable to stop the bleeding, though we had slowed it down. So, we continued—like a seasoned quarterback who drops back in the pocket and sees his first three receivers covered downfield and goes instinctively to his fourth progression. Our fourth progression was to add a blood sealant under the first gauze that we had placed, and then to compress that with three other cigar-shaped gauzes over it. All our practice enabled us to stay calm and focused throughout the process. We succeeded in stopping the bleeding, got proximal control of the artery, then finished the operation. The patient recovered fine and went home in a few days. He never required any blood transfusions or for us to open the chest.

Our surgical team is extremely skilled, and incidents such as this are relatively uncommon after a large experience. You might think something that uncommon wouldn't warrant all the preparation. In fact, it was the practice and preparation that allowed us to swing into fast action when the rare eventuality occurred. If anyone on the team had stopped or stumbled because they were upset, disappointed, or fearful, the outcome might have been very different. Ample practice creates muscle memory, allowing us to drop into the "zone," tune out distractions, and move methodically and calmly through the appropriate protocol.

Omega for the Win

Practice is critical to surgery, and it's just as important in daily life and in honing your leadership skills. My three sons have each been involved with multiple youth sports, and I've coached scores of their teams—sometimes coaching numerous teams in basketball, baseball, and hockey simultaneously in the same season.

My youngest son, Matthew, played with the Cavaliers, a boys' basketball team that I coached. The Cavs made it all the way to the final round of our league championships. Trouble came near the end of the final game. We were down by two points, with just 2.3 seconds left on the clock. All we had left was one thirty-second time-out. We used it to re-review our plan.

With the boys gathered around, I told them we were going to use the play we called Omega. Before I could start running through it, Matthew spoke up. "Dad, we all know

Omega. We practiced it every single day for the last three months."

"Quiet!" I barked. "Now we only have twenty seconds left to review it." Omega was a play in which we passed the ball inside to our best player, Warren, who then kicked it out to Matthew to take a three-point shot. In this case, if the team executed the play properly and Matthew sank the shot, we'd take the championship with a one-point victory.

That's a lot of high-stakes pressure for eight-year-old kids. In the game photo, seen below, Matthew is the boy standing with his arms crossed. You can see that Matthew and his teammates look remarkably relaxed given the circumstances. They had practiced Omega so many times that they had it committed to muscle memory. Verbally running through it during the timeout triggered the memo-

ries to action. The practice paid off, as we executed the plan hit the shoot and won the championship that year.

Transforming Tedium into Joy

People often have strong, negative feelings about practice. This could come from a poor school memory of having to copy a poem thirty times to practice penmanship drills. Or maybe from being forced to practice piano an hour a day while the other kids were all outside playing. Practice requires time, discipline, and commitment, which all often get translated to a sense of drudgery and sacrifice. Engaging each participant's commitment is the single most important element of a team's success. The team must be engaged and they must each—and as a team unit—see the value in practice.

Practice doesn't have to be tedious—even when it's difficult. Take it from the brilliantly talented dancer and choreographer Martha Graham. In her 1952 essay, "I Am a Dancer," Graham showed how practice was deeply integrated into her life: "Practice means to perform, over and over again in the face of all obstacles, some act of vision, of faith, of desire. Practice is a means of inviting the perfection desired."

The way you think about practice—whether you approach it with dread or delight—will affect your ability to practice effectively and to achieve mastery at any stage of your development. Your commitment to practice enhances many of the traits that are essential to leadership, such as competence, passion, awareness, humility, and having a positive attitude.

Practice also needs to evolve and be varied in order to remain fun. Each practice can concentrate on different aspects of the game or project. We call this directed practice, and as highly functional teams evolve and mature, this is the type of practice that should be implemented. It is shorter and more valuable. A great coach or leader develops unique and novel ways to engage his or her teammates in the art of practice. There can be individual directed practice as well, but the team must practice as a whole. It can't become stale or the participants will grow disinterested and less engaged—especially for busy people who have many other roles and responsibilities in life outside of their job.

Sound a little too rosy? The truth is that you're likely to have some internal resistance to practicing leadership skills, especially if you have some long-stewing personal resentments. That's not unusual. Negative inner voices may whisper that practice is a tedious waste of your time. When that happens, just notice the complaining, then calmly direct your attention back to what you're practicing and why you are practicing. The team's goal is always the driving force.

This redirecting process is mental practice that will make you more effective at your job and strengthen your ability to lead. You'll have good days and bad days, but overall, you'll make progress and improve your habits and processes. In my first book, *Super Performing at Work and at Home,* we noted that while high performance may not always lead to positive outcomes, "a commitment to process improvement will always eventually lead to success." The same is true of practice. As long as you're using good technique and practicing the right things in the right way, you'll always benefit from practice.

In that "I Am a Dancer" essay, Martha Graham summed up the value of practice: "I believe that we learn by practice. Whether it means to learn to dance by practicing dancing or to learn to live by practicing living, the principles are the same. In each, it is the performance of a dedicated precise set of acts, physical or intellectual, from which comes shape of achievement, a sense of one's being, a satisfaction of spirit. One becomes in some area an athlete of God."

Chapter 6

Metrics that Matter: Leading the Way to Better Results

Processes, metrics, outcomes. Which of these items is most important to successful leadership? As a leader at any level, which one should you prioritize? That's somewhat of a controversial topic in the world of business management and organizational development.

My original intention with the book, as is my coaching and parenting style, is to stress perfecting your processes, ensure you are measuring the right metrics, and then just let the outcomes take care of themselves. Over the past couple of decades, surgery and other fields have seen a pronounced emphasis on quality and outcomes. Even owning some outcomes, you may not be able to fully control. Are we sure that we could have not fully controlled them? This is process improvement—facilitated by the use of business metrics (standards of measurement). Make no mistake, these are solid methods for delivering better medical care; higher-quality goods and services; and making companies, hospitals, and all kinds of organizations more effective and profitable.

As surgeons, our job performance depends on precision equipment, skill, knowledge, and highly trained personnel, and we are keenly interested in continuous improvement of team processes. However, we are also acutely aware that the purpose of all these intensive efforts is to obtain better results for our patients and institutions.

At the end of the day, it's the outcomes for my patients that matter.

The metrics we apply to improving our processes must be based on the desired outcomes, not just the processes we use to achieve them. Did the patient survive the surgery? Was the cancer removed? Was their quality of life restored quickly? Did we prevent further morbid treatment like chemotherapy and/or radiation, and if we did not, could we have if we had performed the operation sooner or better?

It often happens in life that when we pour energy and attention into one enterprise, we neglect another. The scale tips to one side and we may forget how to bring it back into balance because our ways of thinking and performing have become too rigid and entrenched. Choosing and applying the right metrics matters. Process and quality improvement matter, but don't lose sight of the fact that they matter in service of the outcomes we're seeking to achieve.

Asking the Right Questions

Actor Brad Pitt portrays Oakland Athletics general manager Billy Beane in the 2011 movie *Moneyball.* It's based on the true story of how Beane charted an unorthodox strategy for recruiting players to build a winning Major League Baseball team. After the 2001 season, three of the A's best players became free agents and left to take better offers from deep-pocketed teams. The departures were sure to hobble the A's in their next season. Pro baseball is all about winning games and championships.

At the start of the movie, Beane is sitting around a big conference table with a bunch of scouts, discussing draft prospects to fill the gaping holes on the squad. The scouts favor one player, whom they describe as being good-looking, big, and fast, with a beautiful swing and explosive contact. Much to the scouts' puzzlement, Beane asks, "If he's a good hitter, why doesn't he hit good?" They say he needs time, training, and experience. Beane is not convinced.

Beane then asks the exasperated scouts what problem they're trying to solve. One by one, they chime in with answers: "We're trying to replace three key players," or "We need to hit thirty-eight home runs," and one by one, Beane shoots down their replies. "You're not even looking at the problem." He says the problem is money. Some MLB teams in large urban markets have oodles of it, and the Oakland A's are poor by comparison. They simply don't have the funds for multi-million-dollar contracts. "It's an unfair game. We've got to think differently."

The different thinking that Beane employed—on film and in real life—involved using metrics in a way that deviated from the status quo. In doing so, he thumbed his nose at longstanding baseball recruiting processes, as well as the skill and experience of his scouts and coaches. He stopped assessing players based on star quality or batting average, instead applying outcomes-based metrics, particularly on-base percentage, or OBP. In baseball statistics, batting average only counts hits, whereas OBP includes walks and hit-by-pitch. Beane thought OBP was a more accurate metric in relation to the goal of winning. Today we use many more sophisticated metrics like on-base slugging percentage (OPS) which is the sum of the on-base percentage plus his slugging average.

The idea is that the more players a team gets on base, the higher the chances of scoring runs and notching the win. Whether or not you agree, the point is that it represents a fresh approach to improving processes with different metrics—from the starting point of the desired outcome. Beane was in a jam. His struggling team couldn't afford the big-money players. So, he changed his drafting and recruiting processes by identifying and applying a metric that no one had previously used that way. He began by asking the right questions about the root cause of the problem and the possibility of new kinds of solutions.

But We've Always Done It This Way

Surgeons in academic medical centers typically have periodic conferences on morbidity and mortality, meaning illness and death. We get together and talk about operations we have done or patients we have cared for that had bad endings, operations where the patients had a bad surgical outcome or died. We review one of these thoroughly, looking for missteps or mistakes that will help us learn and improve outcomes in the future.

Invariably, most often I hear the doctor say, "I would have done it all the same way again tomorrow." They don't see anything that varied from strict protocols, nor anything they'd do differently next time, but when a patient dies, it's glaringly obvious that we could have done something differently. It's a question of where and how we look for what went wrong. If every step in the process seems perfect, then let's look elsewhere. Maybe there was something else going on preoperatively that we missed or did not measure. Outcome must drive the analysis of the processes and metrics. Too often we conclude that were unlucky.

My main point is simple:

If you continue to yield a non-desired outcome, and a thorough root-cause analysis and/or process evaluation

cannot identify a problem, then you are not measuring all of the right metrics along the way.

Surgeons and hospitals go to great lengths to ensure that everything is done precisely "according to Hoyle," as the expression goes. We follow the standards and procedures to a "T" because the patient's well-being is paramount. That's as it should be. We consider ourselves to be subject-matter experts in surgery and medicine. It's very hard to admit when we do anything wrong, especially if we didn't know it was wrong or if it was something entirely outside our surgical domain and control.

The life-and-death nature of surgery puts this into sharper focus, but it's true for leaders in any work situation. It's not an either-or distinction between process and outcome. Once you've garnered a strong degree of skill and expertise, there's a natural inclination toward routine, toward doing things the way you were taught, the way they've always been done. With that comes resistance to change, resistance to thinking outside the box, and resistance to considering new metrics and methods that might actually bring better results.

Dogma rules evidence.

My oldest son Rob works in the front office for the Cleveland Indians. He was traveling one day with another front-office staffer who works directly with players. They were debating the issue of batting average as a metric for baseball success, and I called my son to talk and I got into this debate. We all agreed that batting average is a poor metric of quality at-bats or hitting. There are other metrics of hitting that are better, such as OPS that we mentioned above, or exit velocity of a ball off of the bat, or launch angle, power or blast indices. There is even one that we prefer that measures a players total worth both offensively and defensively called "Wins Against Replacement" (WAR). There are many other metrics we can use or refer to in baseball, surgery, or any part of life if we want. I have created one to score surgeon's efficiency and quality that we call the Surgeon's Efficiency and Quality Index Score (SEQI).

The goal of all of these complicated metrics is to optimize the manner in which we score performance in order to recognize the best of the best equitable, given all variables that affect participants' outcomes. Highly functioning teams continuously identify new metrics that adjusted for newly considered or measured variables in order to accurately identify the best. However, at the end of the day, it is the ultimate outcomes that matters the most, not just the process. If the patient dies, it does not matter how well the surgeon did the operation or how high the SEQI Score was. If the batter makes an out to end the game, it does not matter how perfect his at-bat was—the team lost.

As the debate turned heated, I set up an example of a player who comes to bat fifty times in a row. Each time, it's the bottom of the ninth, two outs, there's a runner on third base, and the home team is losing by one run. All fifty times, the batter has a new, perfect at-bat by every granular measure of at-bats that we currently have: he watches balls and only swings at a strike that has a lot of the plate and is good to hit; he hits the ball optimally; the launch angle is ideal; his hand time to the ball is optimal; his contact point to the ball relative to the plate is perfect; his bat velocity is eighty-seven miles per hour; the exit velocity of the ball is one hundred twenty miles per hour; he rakes a line shot right back up the middle, right at the center fielder—yet all fifty times, the ball is only a dep line out into the center-fielder's glove for a game-ending out. I argue to my son and to his friend that this is a failure, and my son and his smart friend, the performance coach, disagree. He did everything he could do, they say. He had a great at-bat, they argue. He did everything he could do to win the game and he cannot control the fact that the center fielder caught it, they say. It was a successful at bat, they argue. I disagree.

They vehemently insisted it was. In their estimation, the batter did everything exactly right. His mechanics were perfect—he swung only at strikes; his bat speed was high; the angle of the swing and the lift of the baseball were highly scored; and he hit the ball hard. They would not have the batter do a single thing differently. I disagree.

The batter's mission or assignment at the plate was to score the runner from third. He failed all fifty times and the team lost all fifty games. How can that be a success?

We must own our outcome and then tweak the process, or our measurements and metrics of the process, to get a better outcome. We must find a different metric that reflects the poor outcomes. **We must ensure we are measuring the things that really matter. The goal was to win the game—the goal for the patient is to go home quickly cancer-free. We do not yet do this in medicine or in surgery.**

Finding the Metrics that Matter

The imaginary batter was the one standing in the batter's box, but it is us who are trapped into thinking this was a "successful at-bat." It may have been a "quality at-bat," as defined by the current metrics we have to measure this, but it was a failure. We lost the game.

If you find yourself or your staff repeating the same procedures over and over without achieving the desired results, it's time to look for new ways to measure the process that you think is so perfect. Look for something you haven't previously considered. Let's suppose a hitting coach told our batter that instead of focusing on hitting the ball hard, he should concentrate on where the ball is in relation to his body when he hits it. Sounds challenging to do in a split second, but elite, professional athletes are fully capable of this kind of visualization.

He could try hitting the ball when it's a little farther out in front, rather than directly lined up with his navel. That might keep the ball from going straight up the middle and instead into the gap in left-center for a game-tying double. It's something the batter could control, the coaches could teach, and the statisticians could measure. Relative position of the ball at the time of contact is not a metric that baseball currently uses too often, but it could prove to be a metric that matters—if they go looking for it, that is. For example, there is new data now showing that greater power is generated if you hit the ball a little bit out in front of you, something I have been arguing to my three boys since they were two years old. My kids have been taught for years to allow the ball to travel as deep as possible. This new data has led to some changes in their approach at the plate. When you insist on sticking to the same methods and metrics, you cannot reasonably expect different results. So, do not be afraid to change based on meaningful metrics. We must evolve or change to get better.

Wait, You Can't Do That...Can You?

Facts are facts. In medicine, we apply proven scientific evidence. This is not to suggest that metrics are magic. You can't alter reality with metrics. What you can do is utilize them to help expand your knowledge base and change the way you think about improving processes to achieve better results.

Remember, though, you need to try out new methods in a testing or practice environment. A lung surgeon wouldn't have the team use a new technique he'd just invented in the middle of an operation. An auto assembly plant manager wouldn't tell his crew to immediately implement his new idea on how to install brakes. Reckless leaders lose the trust of their workers and the loyalty of their customers. Keeping your mind open to new possibilities does not imply that it's alright to ever lose track of your goals, results, or values.

As long as the risks you take are carefully calculated with regard to safety, you certainly can alter your metrics to benefit processes and outcomes. Billy Beane wasn't running a popularity contest on his leadership—and it's a good thing, because he'd have lost such a contest badly during the shakeup. I surprised quite a few parents when I was coaching two of my sons' teams, baseball and hockey, and adjusted the metrics to better align them with the team goals. These were very young teams, with the children still acquiring the basic skills and knowledge of the sports.

Say a kid comes to bat with a runner on second base. He hits a ground ball to the second and gets thrown out at first, but the runner advanced on the play and the team now has a much better chance of scoring and thus winning. The hitter gets nothing for it except a drop in batting average. So on the teams I coached, I gave them a hit. "You just can't do that!" one parent argued. "Really?" I said, "I just did." Now we measure the metric: advanced runners with less than two outs, without a sacrifice. In hockey, all players on the ice when their team scores get a plus-one in their personal stats and a minus-one if they're on the ice when the other team scores. Plus/minus in hockey is as big a deal as on-base plus slugging percentage, or OPS, in baseball.

I wanted to align the metrics to reward players for learning the skills and values that served the team, not just the individual, so I changed the way we kept stats. The batter who made an out while advancing the base runners was scored with a hit. The hockey players on the ice when the opponents scored were given a minus-two, instead of a minus-one. The assistant hockey coach was indignant: "You can't do this! You can't change the way we keep the scorebook." I gave all the players on the ice two points for a short-handed goal.

"Well, I just did for this team this year," I said.

The change only affected our team's metrics, not the scoring of the game. That hockey team developed a great defense as the players vied for the best plus/minus in a way that improved their defensive skills. The Little League players were rewarded with a boost in batting average when they did something that helped the team more than it helped them individually. We aligned our metrics in a team-centric way that was appropriate to the age and skill-level of the team. The players and some parents eagerly bought into the concept. A few adults and coaches remained sticklers for convention.

The Dumbest Metric in the World

Let's look at that Little League team from a different angle. What about the batter with terrible form who doesn't practice to improve his hitting skills? He hits a little infield dribbler and gets on base thanks to a weak opposing team. No official errors are made and a run scores, so the batter gets both a hit and an RBI, or run batted in, on the stats.

Parents and teammates are cheering and screaming, "Great hit; great job!" Actually, it was not a good hit, a terrible at-bat, and the good outcome was a fluke. Celebrate the lucky outcome, sure, but don't make the mistake of depending on flukes to win or pretending they're the same as a solid base hit. There may be two dozen aspects of a good at-bat that we teach the kids and track in our team-centered metrics. Was your stance correct? Did you swing only at strikes? Did you swing hard, hit a line drive? The metrics need to be well-chosen and well-aligned, but not delusional.

One of the most popular metrics in hospitals is O.R. utilization. When I lecture around the world about the business side of surgery, I often call O.R. utilization one of the dumbest metrics in the world. Let's say Dr. Smith is assigned O.R. No. 1 every Friday from 8 a.m. to 5 p.m. Dr. Smith's operations usually run long, and that O.R.'s in use until 10 p.m. every Friday. He only performs two operations in all that time, his patients require blood transfusions, and the outcomes are poor. Nevertheless, Dr. Smith's O.R. utilization rate exceeds 100 percent, and the metrics suggest that he is doing a good job.

Meanwhile, Dr. Jones has O.R. No. 2 assigned at the same time. She performs six operations, needs no transfusions, her patients do great, and she's done with almost two hours to spare. She is performing similar operations with the same difficulty as Dr. Smith. Her O.R. utilization rate comes out to 70 percent. The metrics suggest that her low utilization is bad. So, Dr. Jones, who by all logical measures is a superior surgeon, winds up with less assigned O.R. time over time. That hurts surgeon, patients, and hospital. We are measuring the wrong thing; we need to choose better metrics. And now we have.

The key is to develop numerous metrics that better represent what leads to a good outcome. Again, it's about asking the right questions and measuring the responses. Did the patient survive; did we lose less blood today then we did last year for the same operation; are we doing it faster; yes, time under anesthesia matters—are we getting better every day? Did the team win the game? Sometimes people get so hung up on the minutia of the processes and the granularity of the techniques that they forget what they were working to achieve. You're coaching the player to get a base hit—but the goal has to be team-oriented, team-centered, patient-centered, with the goal of winning the game.

No patient ever comes to a surgeon to improve the surgeon's reputation—they come to get better.

Engagement and Communication

Leaders need to design systems that employ the right metrics—metrics that bring about optimal results that align all stakeholders in the process—insurance companies, hospitals, doctors, nurses, patients, and families. This involves choosing the right standards of measurement, determining the best way to apply and calculate them, and making sure they're accurate. It's a tricky balancing act. Even if management sorts it all out, the organization's leaders will have the job of getting all the team members to understand it and transform theory to practice and create the proper culture that needs to be continuously tweaked.

As we've seen, habitual routines are extremely hard to unlearn and the mental resistance to change can be enormous. This is where leadership comes into the picture. The most important trait on our list for great leaders is communication. With today's high levels of distraction and low levels of attention, effective communication is a challenge that takes patience and a creative, multi-faceted approach that will probably involve teaching the same thing many times in many different ways. Its takes eight to nine times to deliver the same message in order for just 50 percent of your organization to hear it.

You can lecture until you're blue in the face, roll out

clever social media programs, and launch six different multimedia campaigns. However, it will all be for naught unless you get people to engage. They will remain disinclined to adopt new ideas and new methods if they can't understand why they should make the effort. It's critical to get your audience to see how this new information will benefit the organization and, more specifically, how it will benefit them. Even then, you cannot expect to have to stay on message and have to repeat the lesson over and over again, even after they get it and change. It's hard to make the change permanent.

A perfect example of this in the O.R. is preoperative antibiotics—giving the patient IV antibiotics in the O.R. shortly before we make the incision. In lung surgery, infections are so uncommon that this procedure has been considered a waste of time and resources. However, studies have proven that preoperative antibiotics reduce infection and save lives. Still, we couldn't get our surgeons to embrace the idea.

What finally brought a sea of change was showing them that this was being used widely elsewhere to good effect. Failing to implement it was reducing our prized high spot in the national rankings, and maybe persuading patients and families to choose other facilities that offered it. The surgeons finally saw this would save the hospital money and be better for their patients, and that mattered to them. But what really brought them on board was realizing that failing to switch would mean less prestige, fewer patients, and less money in their pockets.

An effective communication plan engages team members, repeats the message as much as needed, offers training, clearly demonstrates the individual benefit, presents ample opportunity for participant buy-in, and allows everyone to feel like they can be part of something that will make a positive difference. That's the road to introducing new metrics and processes that will improve outcomes. Using fear—whether that's leadership by decree, memo, executive order, or a my-way-or-the-highway approach—will only backfire and lead to failure.

The Metrics of Leadership

Leadership is a measurement of the ability to influence and move people. A great leader inspires people to adopt a shared vision and work toward the common goal of the team. This part of our definition of leadership describes the most important element of truly successful leadership: **outstanding leaders inspire and engage their team members and other stakeholders to embrace an idea and make it their own, and work hard to make it a reality.**

To reach the point where you can inspire and engage others, you must be competent at your job and have some degree of knowledge about the work of those above, below, and alongside you in your organization. You also need vision. No, we're not talking ESP. Vision can be learned and cultivated. It is simply a matter of knowing what it means for you, your team, and your organization to succeed. You know the difference between good and bad outcomes, and you can see the path to achieving them.

The metrics used to gauge leadership are as plentiful as in any other part of business. Find the right questions and there's a way to measure the responses. As expected, metrics of leadership include the outcomes, profits, bottom lines, and the number of widgets sold, or services delivered, but it goes far beyond that. Are the people who work with you engaged with their jobs, their work processes, and their departments? Would they take the job again if it were offered to them today? Would they recommend the workplace to friends?

If you are anxious or unwilling to put your own actions as leader under the microscope, perhaps you're not as good a leader as you think you are. Remember that the whole idea of leadership is a constant evolution. It's learning, practicing, improving, measuring, and evaluating. You won't get better if you don't know your own weaknesses and areas that need improvement. Measuring your leadership will help teach you how to capture the hearts and spirits of your team members. It will teach you how to **inspire**.

Chapter 7

Learning Failure

The Oscars, February 26, 2017. Hollywood's most spectacular night of the year, glittering with diamonds and dazzling A-list celebrities. Hundreds of millions of dollars flow like a raging river to cover the costs—clothes, hair, makeup, jewelry, advertising, transportation, media coverage, security, after-parties, and more.

With tens of millions of viewers and so much on the line—at least from the movie business perspective—the last thing the Academy wanted was a humongous blunder marring its final and most prestigious award. Yet that's what it got. Fifty years after they starred in the blockbuster hit *Bonnie and Clyde,* Faye Dunaway and Warren Beatty presented the Best Picture award. It was supposed to be an occasion of honor for them. However, it turned into the dubious task of presiding over the biggest flub in Oscars' history: naming the wrong Best Picture. Leaders, see this as an opportunity to turn mistake and failure into an opportunity to win—in a different way

It fell to Beatty to announce the winner. He opened the red envelope, pulled out the card, and stared at it, raising his eyebrows in puzzlement. Tentatively, he said, "And the Academy Award..." before breaking off and looking awkwardly at the card again. "For Best Picture," he continued, once again pausing, looking at Dunaway, then glancing backstage, as if seeking guidance.

As we later learned, Beatty was mistakenly given an envelope for the wrong category. He held the Best Actress card, printed with the name of the winner, Emma Stone, above the name of the film in which she had starred. Beatty knew that layout was a blaring clue to a mistake. Oblivious to all this because she hadn't yet seen the card, Dunaway was looking for a film name. Her eyes fulfilled her expectation as she instantly sang out, "*La La Land.*"

Cue the cheers, applause, and theme music. A dozen beaming cast and crew of *La La Land* made their way to the stage, and the producers launched into their well-rehearsed acceptance speeches. It was several minutes before the truth emerged, and the stage and golden statuettes were handed over to the crew of the rightful winner: *Moonlight.*

Those few minutes wouldn't be long to most of us, but they sure are in the media—or in a life-and-death situation in an O.R. for that matter. The fumble occupied headlines for days. We learned all the details about the Oscars system, their processes and the mix-up, as well as the cascade of minor incidents that contributed to the chaos. Depending on where you stand, this was either a scandalously epic failure or an amusing reveal of how the Hollywood elite cope with on-camera gaffes.

Let's be real. It was a TV show mistake, not the end of the world. No one died, nor did we take out the wrong lung. *Moonlight* was properly honored. *La La Land's* crew were inspiring for the grace with which they relinquished the cherished award. And for students of leadership, the takeaway includes a host of insights and lessons about how to reduce risks, prevent mistakes, and deal with them when they inevitably occur. Leaders can go the blame-and-shame route, or they can learn how to fail and take their losses levelheadedly. Leaders know how to own their mistakes, take responsibility for them, and change their processes accordingly.

Understanding Risks and Mistakes

All leaders have to take chances. This is true for a police chief deciding how to deploy personnel, CEO of a tech startup launching a new app, or a mother driving her kids to the park. If you're too risk averse—demanding complete surety in every step you take—you may wind up overwhelmed and immobilized. Your business or organization will stagnate. Your children will not learn the life skills they need to become well-adjusted adults.

While risk-taking sometimes promises big returns, as in the stock market, that's not usually true in fields such as surgery or firefighting, where lives hang in the balance and you are risking lives that are not just yours. They require extra measures to reduce risks to the absolute minimum and gauge them against potential benefits. In any arena—whether what's at stake is money, health, safety, or well-being—it's clear that risk should always be as low as possible. But it's hard to think of a situation in which risk is zero.

Some leaders cringe in so much fear and denial about risk that they choke when it's time for action. The better path is to fully know and manage the risks you confront. Thanks to today's actuarial science, there's plenty of data available to inform you about tolerable risk levels and the impact of bad outcomes, no matter the endeavor. Fear is crippling. Knowledge is empowering.

Similarly, leaders want to minimize the number and types of mistakes and to recoup in the most efficient manner when errors occur. Knowledge and preparation are immensely helpful when it comes to mistakes. Leaders need to know and recognize the range of categories of mistakes in case they warrant different kinds of responses. Consider not only what and how things go wrong, but also the scope and impact of the outcome. Some mistakes have few consequences, while others have catastrophic effects.

Jumbo-size mistakes that hurt people or cost a fortune can be caused by small, unforeseen incidents that snowball into something that's greater than their parts. Other times, they're caused by negligence, bad planning, poor training, ineptitude, or cover-ups. With this magnitude of mistake, the situation isn't always fixable.

Another category of mistakes are systematic ones—arising from dysfunctions in the way the system was designed or organized. A professional colleague of mine, whom we'll call Dr. Smith, was a surgeon at a medical center in the Western part of the United States. The department chair was planning to retire, and an executive told Dr. Smith he was in line for the job. He was eager to move up the ladder to the new position.

Unfortunately, a few other surgeons got the same promise from the same hospital leader. Dishonesty is the fastest way to lose all credibility as a leader. I have seen its effect first hand. This conflict led to disappointment, resentment, and a lack of trust that poisoned the air quality throughout the department. Trust is perhaps the single-most important attribute a leader must deliver. You only get one crack at it. You never get it back once you lose it. Smith and other busy surgeons resigned. The hospital leader was later fired, key administrators left, due partly to poor leadership and partly to a flaw in the system design. Management did not have an orderly process in place for internal advancement, effective communication, and transition of power. But make no mistake—it was the lie, the lack of trust, that unraveled the culture.

Leaders should also learn to recognize alignment mistakes. What matters to the employee in terms of the rewards of their work may be different from what matters to the manager. Those values may diverge yet again from what matters to the Board and shareholders. Misalignment of values is a common type of mistake that can lead to financial losses and bad outcomes. As a leader, you may not be able to correct all of the overarching problems, but understanding the nature of the issue may help you find creative approaches that diffuse the trouble it causes by better aligning all the teammates.

Leading Mistakes

The biggest mistake leaders make is in how they handle people. An employee is not a decimal point on a spreadsheet. You can read the tea leaves wrong, make a bad decision, and remain a leader if you manage people well. That entails being honest, accountable, supportive, and humble while creating a safe, open culture for people to learn and improve. Modeling these qualities consistently will earn you loyalty and trust, as well as strengthen your leadership. On the other hand, if you behave duplicitously or selfishly, you'll find yourself isolated, impotent, and resented.

Another problem leaders often have comes from ignoring the elephant in the room. How can you talk about mistakes and correct problems if no one admits they exist? As surgical team leaders, we work hard to create an ambiance that allows us to speak openly about mistakes. We even try to laugh about them—appropriately, of course, and never in the case of a bad outcome. When fear and embarrassment aren't consuming people's minds, they learn better, think more clearly, and make fewer mistakes. We make the discussion of mistakes a learning opportunity, not a blame or gloating session for the other surgeons in the room who also do the same operation—but this patient did not come to them, but their partner.

It's question of allocating mental resources. The person who let the elephant into the room is preoccupied with keeping his mistake secret. Others are wondering if they'll be blamed and who will get tasked with cleaning up the mess. The manager is worrying about how to slip pachyderm-removal costs into the budget without revealing the problem. Everyone keeps glancing surreptitiously at the elephant. Think of all the energy wasted on what's really an open secret. Imagine how much easier it would be if the team could give full attention to discussing the issue and working together to resolve it.

Avoid the Blame Game—Just Own It

Let's go back to the 2017 Oscars for a look at the issue of blame and scapegoating. Each year, after Academy members cast their ballots, a strict and elaborate process is followed to ensure accuracy and protect the secrecy of the results from leaks. It's handled by one of the Big Four accounting firms, PwC, formerly known as PricewaterhouseCoopers. Two well-qualified partners in the company have the job of counting the votes, assembling duplicate sets of winning envelopes, memorizing the full set of winners, and handing the right envelope to presenters backstage at the show.

After the wrong film was announced, several minutes elapsed before the mistake was revealed, as thirty million people watched with dropped jaws. As the personnel shifted on stage, Dunaway stood to the side in stunned disbelief. Beatty went to the mic with a halting, not-my-fault deflection of blame. Host Jimmy Kimmel made a blame-fueled joke and then, with some magnanimity, took the blame himself. In reality, he had no involvement in the mistake whatsoever.

Immediately after the show ended, finger-pointing and speculation spread like wildfire across the media and the Internet. And no doubt among everyone backstage behind the scenes. Who let this happen? Who was to blame? Who would pay the price? Was it staged to improve ratings? As a society, we don't tolerate uncertainty or the unknown very well. While it's always important to prevent mistakes and understand their causes, our obsession with guilt and scapegoating sometimes backfires.

In the case of the Oscars blooper, one person may have had an outsized, but not exclusive, role. One of the PwC partners posted a backstage photo to Twitter just moments before he handed the wrong envelope to Beatty. It would be easy to bring down the hammer on the tweet, but there were other contributing factors to the goof-up that should prompt us to look at the bigger picture. For instance, designers that year changed the envelope colors from gold with bold white letters to red with gold font. The latter had so much less contrast that neither the accountant nor the presenters noticed that the front read "Best Actress" instead of "Best Picture."

Instead of focusing on blame, let's consider all the missed opportunities to avert the error and keep it from escalating. There's no doubt Beatty knew he had the wrong card. When Dunaway prodded him to speed things up, he could have told her and the audience that there might be an error. Why didn't he? Frequently, when the unexpected strikes, our ability to reason logically flies out the window. We see what we expect to see.

This is why in surgery we rehearse, simulate, and drill our responses to the unexpected until they become almost automatic, and enable everyone to speak up. While the stars presenting the Oscars surely rehearse the performance, it's unlikely they'd practiced responding to this kind of accident.

The two PwC accountants were standing close by at each of the stage entrances. They knew *Moonlight* was the real winner because they'd committed it to memory. By all accounts, they both froze. There actually is a protocol for a mix-up of this sort, but they failed to follow it quickly enough. Similar bumbles ensued, until one man took command with a clarity, integrity, and graciousness that sidestepped the blame game and transformed the chaos into a heartfelt moment.

Jordan Horowitz was the leader who took the opportunity of a real-time, non-rehearsed failure (like sports or surgery) to the column of a win. Horowitz, a producer of *La La Land,* had been the first to give his acceptance speech. He was clutching his Oscar and listening to another speech when a stage manager in headset suddenly appeared and showed him the correct Best Picture card. Defining the term "taken aback," Horowitz literally took two steps backwards in shock. Regaining his wits, he walked up to the mic, said, "I'm sorry. There's a mistake." He called out the *Moonlight* crew sitting in the audience: "You guys won Best Picture."

It took a little more persuading to convince everyone of the truth. Jimmy Kimmel apologize guiltily for taking the prize back from Horowitz, who ignored the patronizing and kept hold of the Oscar, saying. "I'm going to be really thrilled to hand this to my friends from *Moonlight.*" This was Horowitz taking unilateral executive action—transforming himself from award recipient to presenter and to a leader.

Horowitz was a winner, a leader, who had suddenly become a loser, but he refused to take on the mantle of loser. He shifted smoothly into leadership mode. With all around him hobbled by confusion, he accepted the turn of events in a way that honored the truth and the meaning of the awards. No blame, self-pity, or resentment were evident. He stayed laser-focused on correcting the error and then wholeheartedly shared the happiness of the winners from *Moonlight.* Horowitz wasn't in charge, yet his every move demonstrated great leadership in action. He saw the mistake—the failure to win—as an opportunity to be a winner—to take that moment and to shake the other teams' hands.

Creating a Safe Culture

The working environments of the O.R. and a film industry awards show are worlds apart in most regards, but there a few parallels. In our thoracic surgery unit, we videotape our operations. We sometimes have viewers around the world plugged in to watch us, live and interactive, where we can answer questions about procedures as we are performing them. We are one of the few in the world to have this type of a system. Mistakes are right out there in plain sight, with individual or systematic flaws fully exposed, and consequences painfully obvious. If mistakes somehow escape notice, we're sure to catch them later, as we review the tapes and study them intensely.

There can be little tolerance for mistakes in the O.R. When you're operating inside someone's chest, a millimeter off or a ten-second delay can have severe results. As surgical team leaders, our job is to be vigilant about reducing risk and preventing mistakes, keeping the threshold for error as low as it can possibly be. Creating a safe culture doesn't in any way mean taking mistakes lightly or viewing them as positive. That could never be the case in surgery.

So, if mistakes are to be avoided like the plague, where's the safety in a safe culture? It stems from the assumption that everyone on the team wants to do their best work, improve their skills, and work toward optimal outcomes. Remember what's at the heart of effective leadership:

Great leaders inspire people to be the absolute best they can be, to strive ever higher as they share values and pursue common goals.

A safe culture doesn't endorse mistakes, and it certainly doesn't encourage a lackadaisical attitude toward them. A safe culture maintains high performance standards. It allows team members to acknowledge mistakes without shame and blame, and to design ways to continually learn from them.

All of this clears the path for a frank, open, and baggage-free discussion about mistakes and the mistake-making process, as well as innovative brainstorming about how to learn, improve, and avoid future mistakes. A safe culture is not a place to hide; it's a place to learn and grow. Great leaders are safe culture creators.

The foundation for a safe culture is built with many of the qualities that are essential to great leadership. They apply to every team member, not just the nominal leader. These traits include humility, accountability, clear communications, authenticity, competence, trust, self-awareness, courage, and service to the greater good.

A well-qualified heart surgeon I know—let's call him Dr. Peters for this story—found himself stuck in an unsafe work environment. Dr. Peters had technical proficiency and good medical judgment. For a variety of reasons, he became pigeonholed for bad outcomes and poor interpersonal behavior. Dr. Peters reacted to the mounting pressure by getting upset during surgery and yelling at other doctors and team members. He knew that if he had another bad outcome, his job was in jeopardy. His confidence shaken, he grew overcautious.

Terrified of making mistakes, he started refusing patients and operations that carried above-average risk. His failure to carry a full caseload burdened other surgeons who had to pick up the slack. He did not feel safe to talk about the problems, and the situation was spiraling downward rapidly. When Dr. Peters behaved inappropriately in the O.R., he'd be officially reported and "written up." As his reputation soured, mutual distrust and enmity grew. In the O.R., there is simply no place for that kind of distrust.

He felt trapped and insecure, unable to envision a path to get himself unstuck from the corrosive situation. After a couple of years of fruitless efforts to improve conditions, Dr. Peters quit to take a position at a different hospital with a more supportive culture. The unsafe workplace had become too toxic to him. His case was a little extreme, but he wasn't the only one. His division had one of the highest turnover rates at this particular hospital system.

Despite stories such as Dr. Peters, building a safe culture is easier than you may think, as long as there's determination to do it. To begin, leaders must set the right tone by taking ownership of their own mistakes. After all, why should subordinates be accountable for mistakes if their boss is unwilling to do the same? This requires a strong degree of humility. A prideful person cannot accept—to themselves or others—that they have erred. However, with the right motivation and effort, humility and accountability can be cultivated and strengthened.

Competing is fine! It's part of striving to be your absolute best. Set your target to excel, to be the Michael Jordan or LeBron James of your field. Just be sure it's positive competition, where you know you are part of a team, respectful of your coworkers and group goals. You're happy for each other, even as you're each trying to distinguish yourselves. Negative competition? That's the destructive, prideful kind, filled with superiority and fueled by cutting others down. It's individuated, centered on ego gratification and personal gain at the expense of the whole. It tends to weaken, rather than strengthen, the team processes and outcomes.

Why Learn Failure?

With all this emphasis on preventing mistakes, why is this chapter called "Learning Failure"? Shouldn't it be about learning to succeed and win, or how to improve your process? The truth is that learning how to take your losses and to fail in a mature, intelligent way is a valuable life skill that is critical to leadership success.

The only road to winning is failing, if you learn how to make failing part of the process and see it as an opportunity.

Once we erase blaming and shaming from the culture of our team, department, or business, failures can become a useful tool to improve processes, systems, and outcomes. Learning failure can serve as the bedrock of leadership. It can form the foundation that forges the mettle of great leaders. I have always told my kids they are so lucky when they lose because they have been given a great opportunity.

Matthews' First Ivy League Baseball Game

Recently, I went to my youngest son Matthew's first Ivy league baseball game at Columbia. After years of hitting him thousands of grounds balls, throwing him over ten thousand pitches righty and lefty, and coaching him in the hot Alabama sun day after day, for dozens and dozens of travel all-stars teams since he was two years old, he finally had his first Division 1 College NCAA baseball game in March 2018. Columbia traveled to Nevada to play the University of Las Vegas, and I was sure to be in the stands to take notes and videos of ways for him to get better. The first ground ball hit to him at second base was a routine ball that should have been an easy double play ball. He booted it and registered no outs, and most importantly hurt his team and pitcher. I turned to the parent next to me and said, "He is so lucky." The father sitting next to me, a knowledgeable baseball fan, thought I was kidding. "Now has an opportunity to learn failure. Let's see how he responds to his next chance, because we know he can't hide and the ball will find him—the ball don't lie." We commonly say this in in our family and in sports, that the "ball don't lie" and "the ball will find you next," meaning that invariably, after an error, another opportunity is coming very soon—and it did. The very next batter hit a tough pop-up to his left over the first baseman's head on a very cold and windy day. Matthew, secondary to his mental toughness and grit, as well as practice and preparation, made a nice play. More importantly, the Columbia Lions got out of the inning without yielding a run. Over the next five games, he made three more errors, but then over the next forty he made only one. He made no errors in the entire Ivy League regular season, spanning over forty-five chances in the field. And despite these facts and his hitting .300 as a switch hitter in the Ivy League his freshman year, he could have performed better and had many opportunities to do so. We know that the "no error" metric is a poor one, in that it does not reflect the many balls he could have gotten to with better lateral and linear quickness. He is engaged in the process to get better, and he will continue to improve by learning how to failure better and less often.

The ideal time to learn failure is childhood. I have three sons, and I played Ping Pong with each of them when they were little. I almost always beat them at these games. My late wife Lorraine would sometimes cajole, "Honey, can you please just let them win once in a while?" Some of my friends poked fun at me. I'd usually let the kids get close, to encourage competitive effort, but I would usually win in the end. I wanted them to learn how to lose, especially a close game—how to get back up when they fell down. Their losses weren't due to mistakes or incompetence in the conventional sense. They came from youthful lack of skill and experience. They hated to lose at first and carried on in a win that prevented them from getting back up to win. Learn how to lose. We disserve our children when we let them win at all the games we play.

Think of a baby who's learning to walk. She pulls herself up, wobbles, makes some tentative movements, and plops back down. Parents who helpfully intervene are doing the baby no favor. They're interrupting a complex process in which the baby's brain is sending and receiving signals packed with sensory information about gravity, balance, coordination, and even the nature of injury and pain. Falling hurts for a reason. **Too many parents provide too**

many cushions for their children's failures. It's the parents' job to know what is age-appropriate and to make sure the learning happens in a safe environment. You would not, after all, let a baby take her first steps on a flight of stairs. But falling should hurt a bit—it's good that it does

My boys were learning how to take their losses for what they truly were—game outcomes, not personal defeats. They were also developing realistic expectations. A seven-year-old isn't going to beat a forty-year-old who's been playing Ping Pong all his life. It's not helpful for them to believe they can. It is healthy to compete, strive to improve, and aim for the stars, but not to focus on unachievable outcomes. If you're a young man who has hit his growth ceiling at five foot five, it's unreasonable to expect NBA superstardom.

At Ping Pong, my sons learned failure effectively because I was careful to make it safe. I didn't deride them for losing, but instructed them where they were weak and how to improve their game, and how to control their emotions while losing to fuel an immediate response at how to win at the very next point—"the ball don't lie—it will find you." The next patient is in the operating room waiting for a perfect operation. We competed hard and we had fun. I gave instruction and encouragement to improve their skills and, more importantly, to teach them to keep losses in context, let go, and move on without rancor. In learning failure, the boys gained emotional intelligence, resilience, and a balanced and realistic worldview. They learned how to pick themselves back up and protect their ego. A pretty good value for the price of a Ping Pong table.

For adults who are leaders or aspiring leaders, it's frankly not that easy to learn failure if you've accumulated a lifetime of emotional misinformation about what losing means. You are, however, always free to choose a different approach, rather than repeating the same behaviors that haven't served you well in the past. Take an honest, introspective look at how you've handled failure and consider whether it's time to try something new.

It's inevitable that you will experience mistakes, losses, and failures—some monumental, some insignificant. Naturally, you'll try your hardest to avoid failing. The lesson is that when things don't go your way, it's acceptable. You don't wrap your identity around the loss and entangle yourself forever. You accept it, learn what you can, then move on to your next endeavor with only the lessons, not the baggage. Great leaders practice this principle, they teach it to others, and they build it into successful organizational structures.

Other People's Mistakes

How many times have you heard that old saying: learn from your mistakes? It often goes hand in glove with the notion that mistakes are inherently good because they bring opportunities to learn and do better. Another common belief is that you can't enjoy spectacular success without first suffering monumental failure.

My experience in the O.R. has shown me that these ideas about mistakes are not the law of the land, either in the workplace or your personal life. There are some aspects of truth in them, as we've seen. You can never completely avoid making mistakes, and you may as well learn from them. Learning how to accept losses and failures is not just a crucial life skill that will enable future successes—it's valuable wisdom. With that said, here's a radical concept: only an idiot learns only from his mistakes. The clever person learns from other people's mistakes and failures. From the surgeon's perspective, mistakes can cause pain, suffering, disability, or death for our patients. We deal in stark realities, even if those realities appear contradictory on the surface. It's a fact that accidents will happen. It's also a fact that our work relies on clockwork precision in which we minimize mistakes and optimize outcomes. It's a leader's role to think about the bigger picture. Besides being a surgeon, I have a Master's degree in Business Administration. We as surgeons are not just trained in operating, but also in operational systems, in how to make departments and medical institutions function more efficiently, achieve better results, and turn profits.

Great leaders will look for ways to integrate learning from the mistakes of others into their organizational structure.

Videotapes of surgery are often shared for educational purposes. Many surgeons like to have any missteps edited out before their peers view the videos. I currently circle my mistakes to highlight them right there on the video. I'll explain how the procedure or technique could have been done better, and then I'll show another video with the right method performed properly. That's an effective way to teach others from your mistakes. It allows them to feel free to show you theirs.

People have criticized me for this, saying, "You're training the competition. Don't teach them all your tricks." But I do teach them all of my tricks. This is about their patients' lives. My so-called competitors are operating on someone's mother or father. In good conscience, we couldn't withhold information that might lead to another surgeon making a fatal mistake, even if it did give my team or hospital a competitive edge. Fortunately, it doesn't. A rising tide floats all boats. Our whole profession improves when we learn from each other's mistakes. In medicine and elsewhere, we should build this concept into our systems.

With the advent of computers and virtual reality, new methods of nearly risk-free learning are emerging, including simulated learning. It can't be considered entirely free of risk because it's a pricey investment and commitment of resources for a hospital or medical center.

In a simulation lab, residents or young surgeons scrub and enter the O.R. to find a lifelike mannequin on an operating table. It has a heart that beats. There's red circulating liquid that simulates blood, a surgical team, machines, alarms, tubes, and instruments. All that's missing is a live patient. The high price tag of some simulation labs makes their value tough to assess. My observation is that they help surgeons learn and save lives. As virtual reality technology advances and new software platforms replace some of the material needs of the labs, the costs of learning through simulation will continue to come down substantially.

Forgiving Yourself

One last bit of advice for leaders in terms of making mistakes and teaching your team to deal with them effectively: learn to forgive yourself. Dr. Grill was an outstanding, fifty-year-old general surgeon who had his first on-the-table patient death resulting from bleeding around the liver. For months after this loss, Dr. Grill was despondent and depressed. He was functioning well under his usual game.

Late one morning, I took him aside in a hallway and told him of the many mistakes I've made. I told him it was time to forgive himself. "We are all just mortal at the end of the day," I said. His face lit up with relief as he realized that forgiveness was something he could allow himself. He didn't need to carry that self-blame around a moment longer. Others did the same thing and finally over time, he went back to being the great physician and educator that he had been prior to his patient's death.

Doctors are often appropriately scorned for arrogance, but the truth is, we are the worst at forgiving ourselves. When we lose a patient or have a bad outcome, we tend to take it very hard and very personally. People put their lives in our hands; it is the highest honor. It's a traumatic experience to walk out of the O.R. and have to tell family members their loved one didn't make it. Of course, it's far more painful for them to hear it than for us to tell them. We know that.

For all the skills at a doctor's command, self-forgiveness usually isn't among them. And it's not the kind of thing they teach us in medical school. Without it, though, we tend to carry our guilt and self-recriminations to the grave—maybe to an early grave.

In fact, forgiveness isn't practiced very well anywhere in our society, even among people who don't face life-and-death situations every day. Too many of us have perfectionistic standards and expectations that we apply internally, whether we realize it or not. When the mistakes and failures come along, we burn up inside. We often lash out at others and try to deflect the blame and guilt we feel. That can amplify the impact of the mistake.

Do everything within your power to avoid errors, be accountable for them, and fix what can be fixed. Then remind yourself that you're not God, you're not perfect, and grant yourself forgiveness. As a leader, a doctor, a parent, or a friend who has failed, once you learn how to truly learn from the failure and how and why you lost, forgive yourself. It doesn't erase mistakes, rewrite history, or bring back patients you've lost. However, it does improve the chances that your team will be better able to accept, cope with, and talk about mistakes and losses, so that you can respond effectively in the future. If you're a surgeon, it makes you better able to apply what you've learned and keep the next patient alive.

Chapter 8

Leadership Styles for a Diverse Team

All of us are motivated and inspired by different things and have different ways we want to be rewarded. As a leader, you've got to learn how to motivate and reward across the diversity of your team. Doing so will make you a better leader. It will also make your team stronger—and more effective.

For starters, consider that your team members may have different basic goals relative to each other and to you. In the O.R., we deal with this in a very material way. Different members of the surgery team are compensated differently. The surgeon gets paid per procedure in most instances, but the nurse and anesthesiologist work for a set rate, so it makes no difference in their paycheck whether we do seven or three operations in a given day. Why would they drive themselves to continuously improve efficiency so that we can do more operations when they get paid the same no matter what? This is the most common complaint we hear from surgeons who are also paid a salary, not per case, but are just naturally driven to do as many operations as they can. We hear this most commonly from surgeons who work in the United States Veteran Administration system or in countries with national healthcare systems.

Most surgeons, however, are getting paid per operation and are rewarded for both greater volume and higher quality, thanks to the quality metrics in our profession. So, we want our team to get better and more efficient all the time. Yet for every eight hours a surgeon spends in the operating room, only three and a half of those hours are actually spent operating. More than 50 percent of the time, we're waiting for the patient to come into the O.R., or we're waiting for the patient to be put asleep, for many catheters and lines to be placed by the anesthesiologists and positioned on the operating room. We stand around and wait for all these various things to happen so that we can actually operate. As the surgeon and team leader, I'd like to reduce that waiting time as much as possible. But when different team members work under different incentives, it can be very difficult to get everyone behind a single set of goals.

This isn't just an issue on surgery teams. In business, you've got salaried managers supervising people who are paid by the hour. To make matters worse, corporate managers often come into the company at the top, without working their way up the food chain. If you've had every single job in the hierarchy, from the mailroom to the factory to the sales floor, you've seen everything, and you understand how it all fits together. That's a valuable quality in a manager. Yet, more often, you've got people at the top who don't understand what their subordinates really do on a daily basis or what their obstacles and challenges are—*and* they're compensated differently. How do you get everyone aligned and working together?

This dilemma is not limited to professional settings. On most baseball teams I coached, one kid is usually hoping that the boy playing instead of him at third base would strike out or make an error in the field, so he could get in the game. His hopes and desire—his value system—didn't match up or align with those of the team's. And in professional baseball there's another kind of divide. You've got the players, and then you have the front office. The players want to earn as much money as they can, while the front office wants to give them the least amount of money as possible. Meanwhile, both groups share the overall goal of winning the World Series. How do you bridge your differences in order to put together a squad that will win the championship?

No matter whether we're talking about a sports team, a thoracic surgery team, or a factory staff making widgets, any team is composed of people who have different backgrounds and different goals. As the leader, you've got to try to align everybody's metrics. That can be challenging, but it's doable.

When we started paying the nurses in our O.R. a bit more for each procedure, rather than a flat rate or a bonus for lower turnover time, an interesting thing happened. Multiple nurses from other disciplines left their teams to come join our team. After that had happened a few times, others in the university decided this was not fair, and I understand their position. But ideally, a similar reward system could be placed in the entire hospital, and not just for those on a particular high-performing service.

"Well, here's an idea," I said. "Instead of pulling us down to the mean, why don't you bring everybody up and raise the mean and enact some type of reward system for all of the operating room nurses in the entire hospital?" This, although a bit complicated, was doable. This did not occur, and, as often happens in large political institutions, the decision to lower the highest performers instead of finding novel ways of raising the game of the mid- and low-performers was decided.

We *should* reimburse nurses for greater quality and quantity, rather than paying a flat rate no matter how they perform.

It's also extremely important to put the team's overall goals into terms that everyone buys into. At a hospital, that's pretty straightforward. The product we're selling is wellness. The patient who lies naked and paralyzed—completely vulnerable to you and entrusting his life to you, on the O.R. table with cancer—is everyone's main concern. Even staff who aren't directly involved in medical services, such as our janitorial team, can get behind the idea of wellness and the notion that everything we do is for the patient. It's easy for a janitor, tech, circulating nurse, and surgeon all to realize, "Hey, all this is for the patient." In that way, we bring people together not just with incentives and compensation, but also through a mission that has a much higher calling and one we all believe in: Give each patient the absolute best experience—not just the best operation, but the best *experience* we possibly can. At NYU Langone Health, we do this incredibly well.

Coach-ability Language

Focusing on a worthy mission is one way of motivating your team. Part of team diversity, though, is the fact that we're all coachable in different ways. Though mission and money are some of the most common motivators, there are a lot of other factors that motivate different people. A **good leader identifies the individual ways that each person is motivated—the person's love language, or what I call their "coach-ability language"—and then devises novel techniques to engage them.** What do each of your distinct team members respond to?

There are some people who feel motivated after getting yelled at publicly, and this fuels their fire. For others, getting yelled at turns their motivation off, even if done privately.

For some people, all you have to do is remember to say, "Hey, you're doing a great job," and occasionally offer a pat on the back to keep them motivated. This type of person may crumble with overtly negative feedback, meaning you have to be thoughtful in the way you offer constructive criticism.

Then there are people who get motivated by seeing the competition. I employed this strategy recently. I have three nurses who are my bedside assistants when I do a robotic operation. Two are very experienced and one is relatively new. Surgeons and surgical assistants all think they are good, including me. I have never met a surgeon who tells me he or she is average, but, by definition, half of us have to be. The surgeon or assistant who may think he or she is good, but is really not, has no understanding of what good looks like. He doesn't know he's below average because he only sees his own work. To address the problem—and knowing it would really motivate him—I decided to show him what good looks like.

To actively correct this process, I often travel, and not only perform other surgeries when I travel, but also to watch other world-class surgeons. This helps me see what good looks like. For bedside assistants, I will often ask one to come into another's operating room, even long after their training is over, just to watch what their colleagues do and how they do it. "Jimmy, I want you to come on this next case and just watch how Lisa docks the robot," I said to him. "I know you do it great, but just watch what she does with a few little things differently from you."

"Look at what she's doing," I said when the operation was underway. "Of course, you can do that, too."

That was all he needed. He realized that she was doing it differently and faster. He got a chance to see what good can look like.

This doesn't apply only to situations in which an employee is lagging. You can do this with married couples or how one set of siblings get along compared to others. Let yourself go out to dinner with a highly functioning couple and learn from them and their marriage style. You may need to individualize your approach in the way you connect with your team members on a basic level. Some people really want to feel connected to their colleagues on a personable level; for these people, I get to know their kids' names. I love to look at pictures of their kids or grandkids. I connect with them on a personal level because that's what they and I truly work for. Most of us work for our families and our desire to make them proud of us at work, as well as at home.

Other people, meanwhile, don't want anybody at work to know anything about their personal life. They just want to come in, do a good job, feel valued, and then go home. And with those people, I never get involved in their personal life.

This played out in an interesting way just a few days

ago, when I had nine visitors watching. An entire surgical group from Germany showed up. I came into that operating room for a robotic surgery and the nurse on duty was Beth, who has a beautiful baby daughter.

"How's your daughter?" was the first thing I said to her. She lit up and gave me a full report. Then I asked about her Thanksgiving and she showed me the latest picture. I asked all about her life at home while she was putting on my gown and gloves.

Two hours later, I came in to do my fifth operation of the day. There was a different nurse this time, a guy by the name of Mitch. He doesn't really like to talk about what's going on at home.

"Mitch, what'd you think of that Alabama game?" I asked. We talked only about sports and work through the entire procedure. Afterward, the surgeon from Germany actually made a comment about it.

"It's really interesting that you're really personal with the one nurse, and the other one much less so." The difference was so pronounced that our international visitors had picked up on it. I explained to them this was my view of their different "coach-ability languages."

This kind of individualized approach is what it takes to build a strong rapport with your team. Even as we're about to perform incredibly dangerous operations, we still have to take the time to care about each person as an individual. As the leader, you've got to figure out how to get the most out of them in order to maximize your outcomes, and this is one way to do it. You coach each one differently to maximize his or her performance.

Indeed, one thing I'm very clear about—with all team members—is that we must be coachable. People are naturally resistant to change. I remind my team that I travel all over the world to watch other surgeons and teams to learn and get better, not just to tell them how we do it. Why should they be any different?

If they want to stick their heads in the sand and not improve themselves, then they're un-coachable. Un-coachable athletes do not play on high-performing teams, and they can't be part of my team, nor do they commonly win team championships. We have to strive to get better in the same way that I decided to switch to a robotic approach for mostly all of my cancer operations relatively late in my career, at an age when most surgeons are afraid to evolve for fear of failing at something new.

Diversity in Leadership

Just as team members have different styles and motivations, leaders have different styles, too.

The coercive method is just what it sounds like; it's the style of leaders who say things along the lines of, "Just do what I say, because I'm the boss." This is not a particularly effective approach, and it doesn't build teams that last. Interestingly, it was the way of surgical leaders in the '80s and '90s in the U.S. and in many countries until today, but it is a failing strategy now.

Six major leadership styles:

Coercive

Authoritative

Affiliative

Democratic

Pace-setting

Coaching

Authoritative means you draw your authority from being the best at what you do: "Come join my team because we're the world's authority." In this style, you try to build your team on the basis of expertise.

An affiliative leader is someone who considers the needs of the team members to be the group's top priority. This is the leader who cares about everybody and is always trying to do right by them, even at the expense of performance and outcomes. Affiliative leaders tend to provide the best healthcare and build childcare facilities at work. Employees tend to love affiliative leaders and will often go to war for them. At the same time, they may not score the highest marks in terms of team performance, or outcome metrics, or profits, but they are often loved.

Democratic leadership is just what it sounds like. In this style, the leader puts everything to a vote. He sends out solutions A, B, and C, and everybody votes, and whichever solution gets the most votes is what the team implements. This might sound like a good way to lead, but oftentimes an expert leader knows the best solution and ends up not applying that knowledge because it's unpopular. This is a slow type of leadership and, too often, large healthcare institutions are like large battleships that lack the nimbleness or quick navigability of a motor boat: when they move, they move a lot of water, but they often move too slowly.

Pace-setting is a very common leadership style in hospitals and, unfortunately, I am an example of it early in my career. I'm the guy who always strove to do the most operations, write the most papers, and see the most patients. However, that doesn't necessarily mark the sign of a good leader. If you are always trying to "beat" everybody else in your mid and late career, team members learn that they can never measure up to you. It is just not an effective leadership style.

The Book—*Inspire*

Finally, the sixth style is coaching. This is the type of leader I strive to be now, as well as affiliative and inspirational. I titled this book *Inspire* because that is how my leadership style is most commonly convened by others. I also thought it was a cute play on words for a lung surgeon who encourages his patients to deeply breathe every day on rounds.

In this chapter, I've described the key aspects of the coaching approach, in which the leader develops individualized plans for each team member. This is the preferred leadership style, and the one most likely to foster a strong team that produces the best outcomes. As a coaching leader, you work with each team member in a personal way to help him get better. You find out what resonates with him and you individualize the plan accordingly. This might sound impossible for leaders of big companies—say, the CEO of a 20,000-person corporation. However, that CEO isn't actually working with all 20,000 staff; she or he has maybe ten top people who report to her directly. So, her job is to come up with individualized plans for each of *those* ten people, not all 20,000.

Leadership is like Golf — Club Selection is Key

Even as coaching is the preferred leadership style, it's also important to recognize that different situations call for different approaches. In the O.R., when we have a patient coding on the table, we don't have time to take a vote about the best next plan of action or to play to each person's strengths with customized directives. We need our team members to do exactly as we say, because we've got about thirty seconds or else the patient is dead. So, we often become coercive. In this way, leadership is a bit like selecting a golf club from your bag: Every leader needs to carry a complete set of clubs in his or her bag and has to choose the right club for a given circumstance.

Each of us has a leadership style that comes naturally to us. No matter how much we study and practice other styles, there will always be a manner that is our natural, go-to approach. I'm not saying that leadership is innate; on the contrary, it can be taught. One key element of this book is that leadership is a teachable skill, and all of us are leaders in one way or another—all of us. That's why I'm writing this book and, I assume, why you're reading it. You can learn to become a great leader. Still, though, there will be a particular leadership style that just fits more naturally for you, whether it's an effective method or not.

The "DiSC" assessment will tell you your natural style, and I strongly encourage you to do it. DiSC stands for Dominance, Influence, Steadiness, and Conscientiousness. If you discover, for instance, that your natural style is dominance, you might not like that. You can work on developing another approach, and you may even become adept at it, but the style that comes most naturally to you will always be dominance, and studies suggest that no matter what you do to change it, you are what you are.

My son taught me a lesson about this when he was only seventeen and was serving as the captain of his high-school baseball team for the second year in a row. Though I now try not to say too much while the game is going on for my third son, like I did for the first two, I take a lot of notes through the entire game. Having been a coach of over fifty Little League teams, it's hard not to always be a coach. At one particular game in Matthew's senior year, I watched his team lose. And I took a few notes.

When Matthew came home that evening, I had a talk with him and challenged him.

"Listen," I said to him. I was a bit irritated. "Your team needed a vocal leader in that last inning. They needed someone to get up in their mug, get on them, tell them to wake up, and stop the mental errors."

And he, my youngest son, looked at me and said, "Dad, that wouldn't be true to the type of leader I am. That's the kind of leader *you* are. You make big speeches; you get everybody riled up—you are a rah-rah guy. I don't do that. I'm not that guy. I will get on people occasionally, but I pull them aside to do it. I rarely give a big speech. They would have known it was fake, and they wouldn't have responded to it."

It was a remarkable piece of wisdom and insight that he already knew the type of leader he was and wanted to remain genuine to it. And yet, at first, I didn't appreciate it. Instead, I berated him more.

"No, great leaders have different styles and know when to implement different types of leadership!" I insisted. "Great leaders know when to invoke one style or another. You would have had a chance to win that game tonight if you had implemented a different style. You needed to be vocal there," I persisted. "It was needed at that critical moment, and you let it go by."

I went to bed thinking I was right, because I always think I'm right.

But by morning, I had realized my mistake. When I came home from work the next day, I called him downstairs and hugged him.

"You taught me something, man," I told him. "You were right. I was invoking what *I* would have done, instead of listening to what you said. It's incredible to me that you understand leadership better than me at seventeen than I do at fifty-four, and I'm the one writing the leadership book."

"Dad," he said, "that's because you've been talking to me about leadership and leadership skills and styles since I was three. You have taught me a lot how to lead."

Matthew relied on his natural leadership style. When he needed to have a talk with an individual team member, he did so in a way that was authentic to his style, which was by taking that player aside, usually not even during a game. He made his teammates better because of it. He made them forgive themselves, and he helped them get better, and they looked up to him.

As leaders, it's our job to use the resources and styles available to us to give our best effort at helping our team members improve and own our outcomes. *That's* leadership.

Chapter 9

Crisis Leadership in Action

Checklists Are Not the Answer

There has been a large move in surgery over the past decade to make hospitals and operating rooms safer, like in the airline industry. The analogy between pilots and surgeons has been more than overdone, and the preoperative checklists that hospital lawyers have promulgated grow increasingly longer and sillier day after day. They are a prime example of non-valued, added steps of improperly protocolled process that are jammed down employees' throats daily. They do not provide any patient safety, and MD's have been sidelined by this silliness. Checklists are important. They make sure we have the correct patient and the correct side—but you do not need to ask twenty-seven times what allergies a patient has. Or, even sillier and more wasteful, where the fire extinguisher is prior to a skin incision every single time when it is in the same spot it was an hour ago when you did the first fire time-out. Yes, it is good to check that it works and where it is quarterly, but not seven times a day.

Team Error Management Can Be Practiced

Checklists are good because they prevent errors of omissions. However, these are rare errors in surgery. We are wasting huge amounts of valuable time, as well as people's energy and patience. We should be teaching how *"we react to errors as a team."* Since no matter how long the checklist grows—and it grows by the minute every day in operating rooms I visit—it will never prevent all errors. And since every system, human or machine-led, will err, the key for a great team leader is to learn how to manage the error as a team, not just as an individual—just as Matthew did in his very first Ivy League game in Las Vegas.

Great teams problem-solve and remain calm when errors occur. They almost seem to like the chaos. I have one nurse who always said that I was a "chaos lover" who loved when multiple emergencies and/or disasters were going on for patients all over the hospital. And she's right, I did, because I loved having the opportunity to solve all of them by the end of the day and having every patient do great. Not enough teams practice error management—how to react mentally and physically to different errors. Yet we should.

Several years ago, I operated on Tami, a cute little blonde-headed girl who was about two and a half years old. She had cystic fibrosis and her lungs were destroyed because of it. Her right lung was chronically infected and spilling infected material into her only remaining functioning left lung. She had not one but two previous operations in her right chest, with parts of the right lung removed; the fact that she'd been operated on previously made our job even more difficult. When a surgeon has to go back into someone's chest or another body cavity, we call it a "redo;" well, this was a "redo, redo." Previous operations cause adhesions and make the job dramatically more difficult, and our job was already risky enough. The operation we were doing this day is called a completion pneumonectomy—that is the removal of the rest of the remaining right lung that had been partially removed in the past.

Her dad was a surgeon, and the family had come to us and our team from California. They had seen a few other surgeons at large, famous medical centers. One suggested the operation was too high-risk and that the little girl wouldn't survive, so he declined to do it. He was a smart and experienced surgeon whom I know well and have great respect for. Her medical doctors had been treating her with antibiotics, but that was insufficient. But as her dad accurately said, "Tami's chance of dying without the operation is essentially 100 percent, so the operation cannot be more risky." He was right. By the time she came to our O.R., this little girl was on a ventilator.

One of the main goals of this operation is to prevent

the infected material in the right lung from spilling into the left, destroying its ability to oxygenate and ventilate (remove carbon dioxide). There are large arteries and large veins that go to the lung, and then there is the airway as well. In this particular type of operation, it's important to try to divide the airway early in the case to stop the spillage. Because we were operating on her right side, the patient was lying on her left. That makes it easier to perform the procedure, but it also means that we are essentially grabbing the right lung, which is a bag of infected pus, and actively spilling infected material into her left lung, which is lying dependently as we operate. Of course, we were well aware of this issue and had prepared for it. We put a suction catheter in the trachea to help suction out the infected material as we were operating before it spilled into the left lung. We also planned to divide the airway early. That way, as we manipulated the lung to remove it, the pus wouldn't spill into the other lung.

The operation started off well and Tami was doing great. Things were progressing along smoothly. Just after I cut the right main bronchus (the airway to the right lung), the anesthesiologist called out in an anxious but professional voice: "I'm not getting any carbon dioxide back. We're not ventilating her, and her arterial saturations are plummeting."

"What the hell do you mean, you're not ventilating her?" I yelled. This took me by surprise. I thought we were prepared and had just "bronched" her to ensure the tube was clean before I cut the right bronchus. This news didn't make any sense. I had the cut the airway and had it clamped off. It was closed. She was on a ventilator as they gave her large breaths of oxygen that should've gone only into her left lung, and the carbon dioxide in the left lung should now be coming out into their system. She *should* have been able to breathe or ventilate just fine; she had Cystic Fibrosis, but it was not that bad. And here he was telling me there was no CO_2 coming out of the tube and no oxygen going into her left lung. This is not compatible with life—she was quickly dying in front of us. Then, dramatically, her heart rate slowed from this lack of oxygen and carbon dioxide buildup, and then it stopped.

I quickly opened her pericardium, a sac that protects the heart, injected epinephrine into it, and then started careful, gentle cardiac massage on this little, fragile, tiny heart. We were jump-starting her heart between my two hands as we worked the ventilation problem and problem-solved what was really an oxygen and carbon dioxide issue, not a heart issue. The heart arrest was a victim of the inability to get oxygen to it and carbon dioxide out of the bloodstream. We had to be delicate; if you compress the heart just a bit too hard, you can easily injure it, and I remember thinking how small and frail her heart tissue was, but we had to get oxygen into her blood quickly.

Her heart rhythm came back a little, but not much. I ripped the O.R. sheets off her face to ensure the tubing was attached. I was problem-solving this fast. This little girl was blue and dying, and/or was going to get an anoxic brain injury.

"Oxygenate her, come on Tami!" I yelled to the anesthesiologist.

"I can't," he said.

"Put a bronchoscope down into the airway, make sure it's not plugged. Make sure all your lines are plugged in and the tubing is not twisted and not loose." At that point, I thought maybe one of the tubings had come off.

"No, I'm bronching, it looks okay, my tubing's okay. We just can't oxygenate her."

Now I had to go back to my algorithm. "Think," I said, to calm myself down. It is common for cardiothoracic surgeons to have to problem-solve in situations like this, especially congenital cardiac surgeons. You have to calm down and think while everyone around may be yelling and scrambling to get things outside the operating room as the patient is coding.

"Think," I said—there are only a few possibilities it can be. We made sure everything on our end—the surgical end—was OK. This was the third time I had done this. The airway is closed—check. There is no blood in the left lung—check. The tubing is not twisted—check. I knew the problem had to be on the other end. I quickly lifted up the surgical sheets that went up to the head of the bed and checked the anesthesia end of the equation.

Thanks to the first epinephrine injection into Tami's heart, it was beating again, but her oxygen was still so very low, and we were about to have another cardiac arrest. We had to get oxygen into her bloodstream in the next thirty seconds or she would die. Sometimes people hit the wrong button, for nitrogen instead of oxygen, so I confirmed that the ventilator was hooked up and it was on oxygen. We checked that *twice*.

The lung may be full of blood or fluid, but that wasn't the case. The right lung was already out of the equation. The only thing left was the left lung and a possible tube occlusion that would keep the oxygen from flowing into her one working lung. The anesthesiologist had already ruled that out—but *then* we realized that had to be wrong. There was nothing else it could be, and we were running out of precious time. The only thing left was that the tube was clogged somewhere, but we could not see where. They had just bronched her and told me the tube was wide open. But as I examined the tubing I noted that at the top of the endotracheal tubing there was a large, thick mucus ball that had blocked the connection between the two tubings. You could not see it because of the attachment. This thick mucus plug was preventing the gas flow of both oxygen into her lungs and carbon dioxide out—and it was killing her. Now, though, I couldn't clear it out. Picture it like a piece of bubble gum stuck in the end of a tube. We tried to suck out it but couldn't.

"Just get us more tubing," I yelled, and the nurse quickly handed me one.

Soon we got precious oxygen back into her system. Thank God! I scrubbed back into the surgical field and we finished the operation.

This entire process took about one and a half to two minutes—too long, but not long enough, we hope, to injure her brain. Maybe that doesn't sound like a long time, but it was an eternity to us in the operating room. In that time, she could have had anoxic brain injury. Miraculously, after we re-established gas flow, she was fine. It was like nothing happened. Three minutes later, her oxygen was perfect, her heart was perfect, and we finished the operation. Thank God she was young and able to tolerate a few minutes of low oxygen. By the grace of God, Tami woke up just fine from anesthesia and asked for her favorite stuffed animal, a zebra she named Sara. Both Tami and Sara did great and went home in a few days.

Preparing for the Worst

I think about that day all the time. I think about the mistakes that I made, that we made. Faced with a crisis, I circled multiple times through the things I could control. I gave the patient a second intra-cardiac injection of epinephrine, which was probably a mistake. I jabbed another needle into her heart when I should have gotten more quickly to what was happening on the other side of the table. This took two minutes, which could have done irreparable damage to her brain. Instead, I should have gotten to the root cause of the problem sooner. A better leader would have. Just because we got a good outcome does not mean we handled the situation optimally. We had not.

Never confuse a win or a good outcome, or an optimal performance or process.

It's important to trust your team, and yet there are also moments when you *can't* trust your team. You have to recognize, in the face of a crisis, which type of moment you are in. When that little girl Tami went into cardiac arrest, there were only so many things that could have caused it, and we checked everything on our end three times—twice was enough. That was not a situation to waste precious minutes trusting the other factors or variables. I should have problem-solved quicker and checked them sooner. My failure to do so almost cost that child her life. That is the way to look at it and not blame your teammate at the end of the table

Crisis situations are the real test of the culture you've created in your organization. To prepare for crisis, you've got to look at your day-to-day culture. Your team members have to trust each other *and* feel comfortable questioning one another. As we've talked about in earlier chapters, it's absolutely imperative that you as the leader set an example in which you draw attention to your own mistakes and allow others to learn from them. When that's your everyday culture, you're building the kind of team that will identify problems and solutions quickly when the stakes are high. When we were operating on Tami, the problem was how long it took me to reconsider what the anesthesiologist had said. I needed to identify his error, just as I may have identified one of my own, and I needed to do it quickly. Teams can and should videotape their interactions, especially in times of crisis, and watch how they problem-solve together as a team. Team responsiveness to crisis can be practiced and should be.

This applies to a lot more than just the operating room, though in most other fields you have more than three minutes to find the answer. Crises happen in corporate boardrooms, and executives try to parse why they're losing money. They go through the different variables. They have more than three minutes, certainly, but every wasted minute will cost them in staff morale. No matter who you are or what industry you're in, rapid problem-solving matters. There are plenty of organizations that are paralyzed by surveys, or consensus, or democracy. In urgent situations, that can leave them immobile; they're like the giant battleships we referred to earlier, large and powerful, but not nimble speedboats that are more agile and often zip by.

Sometimes the leader just needs to grab the steering

wheel without waiting for consensus or worrying about hurting someone's feelings. In some cases, everything will depend on the leader's ability to do precisely that.

To cultivate that ability in yourself, think about how you do or do not read the signals that are available to you. If you're out of touch with what's happening on the ground, you might think you're gliding down the highway at sixty-five miles an hour and everything's perfect. In fact, your organization may have veered off the roadway and be heading towards a cliff. One of the biggest mistakes a leader can make is not having his or her finger on the pulse of the organization.

To address this problem, work on becoming a better listener. Vow to listen more and with greater depth and in different spheres of your organization. Pay attention to the signals and evaluate.

You cannot meet with your team members or stakeholders often enough.

How does what you're hearing from your team challenge, complicate, or confirm what you already know? I have seen several surgical leaders so out of touch with how they are perceived it's amazing. One recently was telling me how well liked they are and how well they are doing, and he has no idea how poorly most think of him. Persistently ask for anonymous feedback and have an open door for criticism to hear it to your face, as opposed to words behind your back.

Then, take responsibility. A good leader empowers his or her team members in the field so that each person takes responsibility for his or her work. (You'll find more about this in the next chapter.) But when things go wrong, the buck stops with you. I made a mistake when Tami was turning blue on our O.R. table. My mistake was not holding myself accountable for everything that was happening, outside the intra-operative realm including the tubing that the anesthesiologist had inserted. He's a very skilled anesthesiologist and very experienced, but that was a unique situation, and I should have been more tuned in to the other possibilities, especially given the thick secretions she had. While a good leader delegates and then allows his people to do their job, at the end of the day it's the leader who is responsible for the outcome. Remember: you put them in that position in the first place.

One of the best ways to prepare for crisis is to simulate and practice. What better way to see how your team will react to an emergency than to watch them do it? We use this method in the O.R., of course. We put people in simulators and see how they respond. We videotape every operation we do. Boardrooms can practice simulations as well. Frankly, this method should be used much more widely to prepare for many types of circumstances.

I suggest we videotape our arguments with our loved ones, but few agree to this. It's easy to do with the ubiquitous nature of smartphones. What better way to argue better and more fairly and reduce further arguments? Let's go to the videotape. Here is what you said and how you said it.

Simulations are so effective for one very important reason. When you simulate stressful situations, it's a way of helping your group see that external stimuli don't dictate your response.

***You* control your behavior, no matter what's going on around you. If something terrible is happening, you still have the power to stay the course and do what you know is right, no matter what others are saying or doing, or how they may be out of control.**

The more you simulate problem scenarios and the more you simulate game-day, the more you'll help your team develop more skills in their toolbox, and the more likely you'll get the right outcomes under pressure. This elevates the team's responsiveness to crisis management, not just each individual. And that is the ultimate goal to have a team that performs well on "Team Error Management."

Of course, another crucial dimension to dealing with crisis has to do with accountability, which we will discuss in the next chapter. Will your team members step up or want to step up when it matters most?

Chapter 10

Creating Accountability

On highly successful teams, everyone is accountable for everyone else's actions. There's a lot of focus today on "do your job." I'm not suggesting that's a bad thing. If you do your job and the other guy next to you does his, then ultimately, you're going to win. That's certainly the way it works in the O.R., but on most teams, jobs overlap, and good teammates help other teammates to "do their job" when they can and their teammate can't do their job. But first you have to know what their job is—how it integrates into the entire team picture.

As you saw in the last chapter, things don't always go according to plan. And the best teams are the ones in which teammates step up to help one another and in which individuals hold themselves accountable for the overall product. I believe that's the very definition of accountability. Accountability is much more than just taking responsibility for your own work. It's taking responsibility for your entire team and for your entire team's outcomes.

The truth is that without accountability, a team eventually will become dysfunctional. There's no such thing as a road without any bumps in it; no matter what industry you're in, problems will always arise, and there will always be complications that you didn't expect. And a team without accountability will not be able to meet those challenges. Instead, you'll have a situation in which everyone believes they have only narrow responsibility for their immediate tasks and everyone says, "Well, I've done *my* job." No one will step up to deal with a sudden problem or emergency; no one rises to the occasion. That, in turn, fosters resentment between team members, and that's when it starts to crumble. I have seen this commonly in teams that are unionized. Team members start to leave, and the operation falls into a downward spiral.

Instead of permitting that kind of race to the bottom, it's your job as a leader to create a race to the top: a team environment in which everyone steps up when something goes awry. That creates a sense of mutual responsibility, camaraderie, and trust. Where does that race to the top begin? With you, the leader. You can pick up the other guys' job.

As I mentioned briefly in the last chapter, good leaders delegate. They find team members they trust, they empower them, and then they leave them alone to do great work.

That's a hallmark of a great leader. And then never become envious if they outperform your expectations and get high praise for doing so. You leave your people to do their work and do it well. And yet, at the very same time, great leaders never shy away from taking bottom-line responsibility for what their teams produce. That might sound like a contradiction: how can you assume responsibility for other people's work if you've genuinely empowered them?

The answer has to do with those bumps in the road. When things are going well, and your team members are consistently hitting their mark, they get credit and praise for doing so (more about praise-giving soon). When things go awry, though, you're the one who's ultimately responsible. You've got to provide the feedback necessary to help them improve, of course, but at the same time you model accountability by taking responsibility for the screw-up. That's how you create a culture of accountability: you model it.

We do this in the O.R. on a regular basis. One day, I had a medical student actually keep track of the number of mistakes we made as a group. I helped her count each one. There were fourteen mistakes total; I acknowledge all of them, including and especially my own. Then I expect my "subordinates" to do the same, and I'm very open and direct about that. I said to one medical student, "When I asked you to bring the needle into the subcuticular part of the skin at a specific angle, we need you to do it and do it quickly." These fourteen errors were all very minor mistakes, and no one got hurt. The point is that we use teachable moments in real time to build accountability.

Those mistakes offer a precious opportunity to practice for much bigger ones that lead to bad outcomes.

The fallacy is that mistakes that lead to bad outcomes are the only ones to track. This is wrong. There are hundreds of small mistakes that do not lead to bad outcomes, but could. This is why we review the films on all of the operations we do, to look for opportunities to get better, not just focus on the ten seconds of film when a disaster occurred; everyone does that. I commonly see this mistake by sports announcers in baseball.

"Jim pitched a great game today, Billy. He only made one mistake on this fastball that was hit for a home run," referring to the one home run he gave up. I hear this every day. Nothing could be further from the truth. It is a silly statement. All three of my boys pitched, and I could show them forty bad pitches, forty mistakes in a complete-game, nine-inning, 2-0 win. They often got away with several bad pitches. Just because your opponent did not capitalize on that particular mistake and hit a home run off of a bad pitch does not mean that you only made one bad pitch. The truth is you made several.

In the story I told in the last chapter about the little girl Tami whom we operated on (who ended up doing just great), success does not mean that we cannot get better and improve our process. Don't let any mistake small or large go by without helping the group learn a better strategy for the future. A good outcome does not mean that the process cannot get better.

Indeed, when something goes wrong, you've got to step in swiftly to correct matters. You correct the individual, if needed, just as you expect him or her to correct you. When my team makes a mistake, we own it—or "wear it," as I like to say using sports lingo. I often say to the kids I coached in baseball: "OK, guys, we made a bad error now; as a team you have to wear it." The kids love that expression, and it's a really effective catchphrase to help them own up to their mistakes. We wear our mistakes, we admit them, correct them, and then we move on. Most importantly, we do not let them roll into another one. We reset and start anew. Poorly functioning teams often let one error by one teammate lead to a second error by another. We commonly see this in Little League baseball. In surgery, while coaching surgeons, I often say:

"It is never the first mistake that takes the patient's life; it is the second. So, after the first one occurs, it's over. It is in the past. The next step is not related to this last bad step. Relax, take a deep breath, clear your mind, go into team recover mode, and go back to being highly functioning. Live in the present, live in the moment, go through your routine, reset, and go back to performing at a high level."

Real accountability also means that you never blame a team member. For example, a surgeon must never say to a patient, "I'm really sorry that the nurse gave you the wrong medication last night and you had this reaction to it." Accountability means that everyone is responsible. It sounds like this:

"I'm sorry we gave you the wrong medicine last night. You will be fine and there are no others steps we need to take to make sure you are OK. You were not hurt by this mistake in any way. However, we'll make sure it doesn't happen again. I'm sorry you had this problem. Everyone is aware of what happened. I apologize to you and your family. We have enacted a new process so this never ever happens again to you or another patient."

Through this approach, you'll foster a sense of accountability in each team member, as well as *between* team members. As I've discussed in previous chapters, it's essential to establish a culture in which you openly review mistakes and learn from them together.

Interestingly, this approach to accountability can sometimes be the most difficult for the most skilled team members. You might find that your highest-performing employees don't want to be held accountable for their peers' mistakes; after all, *they* are doing a great job, so why would they want to answer for weaker teammates' problems that occur in a silo that they are not even part of? While we understand that sentiment, it doesn't fit with the values of the team. Our collective job is to serve the patient, and we do that as a cohesive whole.

And that's exactly how we help reorient the talented members of my staff who resist taking responsibility for the work of others. I make sure they're aligned with the mission. In our case, the mission is for the patient to do well. Our mission is not just for a single medical student or nurse or anesthesiologist to do his job well; it's for the *patient* to do well. And for that to happen, everyone must be accountable.

When this is your mindset, it eventually becomes second nature to step up when someone else fails. Many days, my staff can't shave the patient for a procedure. So, I get the razor and shave them myself, commonly. What no one said was, "That's not my job!" We pick each other up all the time, day after day. That's just our nature now and our response based on our values and our mission statement. Every single time we step into the O.R., we remember that the work we're doing is bigger than any one of us. It is about that patient.

Another dimension of accountability—and one that's often overlooked—is giving credit and praise for a job well done. As a leader, it's at least as important for you to call out success and give credit as it is for you to call out mistakes. You should give more positive feedback than negative. Many of us are inclined to focus more on the negative than on the positive. Yet part of true accountability means acknowledging successes and encouraging team members to take credit for what went right.

One day, my team performed a very difficult operation to remove a tumor that had started in the lung and grown into the first rib. This is called a Pancoast tumor, and the patients get radiation and chemotherapy first, which make the operation more difficult, and we did it robotically. This required different instruments that we don't normally use. My scrub nurse actually went out and borrowed instruments from the neurosurgeons and the orthopedic surgeons so that we had everything we needed. The procedure went very well—thanks in no small part to her contribution.

When it was over, I called her into my office and closed the door. Then I told her what a great job she had done finding all the instruments that we needed in order to perform the surgery.

I'll be honest with you: This is not my strongest area. I don't spend enough time giving credit where credit is due. On the day we did that operation, we had only five cases. If we'd had eight, as I usually do on my operative days, I wouldn't have made the time to take that nurse aside and tell her what a great job she'd done. So, this is one area in which I'm trying to improve my own leadership skill. I've got to get better about taking time to give credit. Not over e-mail after the fact, but in person, eye to eye. As leaders, all of us should strive for this.

More complicated than giving praise or credit is addressing the problem of an employee who has become disengaged. This happens even in the very best team environments, usually because the employee is struggling with something very difficult in his or her personal life or has begun to feel he is no longer appreciated at work. This happened with someone I know who served as an administrative assistant. I could see that she had disconnected from her work and that she wasn't all there in the way that she used to be. Well, it turned out that her and her husband were having real problems at home. She had always done great work, so this was a moment for me to show that I valued her as a person.

"Take a few days," I told her. I reminded her of how much she had done for our team, and I encouraged her to take the time she needed. She ended up getting a divorce. Afterward, she remained on our team because she could tell that we cared about her as a person.

In that case, I was dealing with a great team member whose work had suffered for personal reasons. But what about a team member who is trying his or her best but just doesn't have the skills to do the job? My rule of thumb is that anyone who is aware of his weaknesses but is striving to improve is someone I want on my team; I'll usually find a role for that person and keep him or her around. This requires honesty; "you can still be a valuable member of the team doing this."

This has happened several times, and I consider it my responsibility to help them become the best in whatever job they can do. Occasionally, though, I'll encounter someone who doesn't get it. One person had their heart set on becoming a cardiothoracic surgeon, but they just didn't have the technical ability to do it, and there comes a point at which that's very obvious. This person had already been asked to leave a different cardiothoracic program. When they joined our team, I told them in the first three weeks that they didn't have the technical proficiency to be a cardiothoracic surgeon.

"Let's get you the skills to be a great general surgeon," I said. It was clear he could succeed at some parts of general surgery, but not at cardiothoracic surgery.

"No, no," they said, reiterating that they wanted to be a heart surgeon. "That is what I want to do, and I can do anything I set my mind to," they said. "No, you can't," I responded. "It does not always work that way. You have been trying to do this now for forty-two years and multiple well-respected people have told you, you can't do it, and now I am telling you the same thing. At some point you have to listen to others and be honest and true to yourself."

My job in that situation was to be honest. This surgeon didn't have the right stuff, and it was a waste of everyone's time—especially theirs—to let them believe otherwise. I tried to help them gain awareness of their God-given limitations. In surgery, as in certain other fields, there are simply some hard limits on what some people can achieve. Not everyone is cut out to be a surgeon, and of those who are, plenty aren't right for thoracic or lung surgery.

Dealing with that situation is one of the harder things I've had to do. It's awful to tell a forty-year-old individual who was at the top of their medical school class and who did well in a general surgery residence that he or she can't make it as a lung surgeon, even though it has been a life-long dream. All of their life experiences indicate that they should just work harder. So, they worked harder and harder. But sometimes hard work is not enough.

Far simpler is the matter of dealing with people who are unaware that they're incompetent *and* don't share your values. In the story I just told, the would-be thoracic surgeon was trying as hard as they could to improve. However, there are plenty of people who believe they're competent or, even scarier, actually good, when they're in fact not and who refuse to work hard to improve themselves. I maintain a very, very low tolerance for that. They get a warning or two, and then they have to be kicked off the team. We take responsibility for the work of each of our employees, but I can't do that for a person who's not dedicated to getting better.

At the end of the day, the key lesson of accountable leadership is relatively simple:

From the CEO to the lowest-ranked staff on the organizational chart, everyone must be accountable for more

than his or her immediate job. This is about taking responsibility for much more than your own work; it's about wearing the successes and mistakes of your entire team and stepping up to tackle any challenge in the instant that it appears.

Chapter 11

Using the Surgeon's Toolkit: Operating on Your Organization to Improve Outcomes

Just about every surgeon in the world wears what's called a "surgeon's headlight." It's nothing like the type of headlamp that you can buy at an outdoor supply store, nor is it like the flashlight that you probably keep in the glove compartment of your car. The surgeon's headlight gives off a profoundly intense white-blue light that illuminates everything—every freckle and every blemish. Nothing can hide from it. As a surgeon makes smaller and smaller incisions, the headlight becomes more and more important, because you need ever more intense light to illuminate the operative area now through cameras.

However, it's not just surgeons who need an intense light shining on the problems they face. Every leader needs to be able to zoom in on very specific areas of their organization in order to diagnose and correct problems. All leaders need to be able to turn that light on themselves; few tools are as important as the ability to scrutinize your own leadership ability. We have spent twenty-one years building and leading one of the best surgical programs in the world, but I still regularly need to shine that bright light back on myself—and what I find is still frequently disappointing.

In fact, one day I yelled at one of my medical students. I barked orders at him like I was a younger version of myself trying to assert my authority. I was performing an operation, early in my day with a schedule of eleven that day. And when I turned around, I accidentally contaminated my glove on the student who was standing too close behind me. How did I respond? By immediately yelling: "Come on, man! Why are you so close to me on a case where you can see everything on camera? You should be sitting in a chair!"

In that moment, I didn't stop to think about my reaction. While there are times in the O.R. when a surgeon absolutely *has* to be able to bark orders—because someone's life depends on it—this wasn't one of those times. Only after it happened did I think to myself, *Why did I yell at that guy? Why did I get so mad so quickly? Because I was stressed with the big day and it was just starting. I hate to start late.*

This is the real significance of the white-blue light of the surgeon's headlight: It's a metaphor for turning your analysis on yourself and your organization in order to seek out and understand all the blemishes. Earlier in this book, I mentioned the idea of doing a 360-degree review, and that's a great start for shining a light back on yourself, but the truth is that a 360-degree review is just the beginning. You can go deeper. What you find may not be very good, and you may not be proud of it. I'm not proud of yelling at that guy, and I'll never learn to do better if I don't try to understand what was going on for me in that moment.

A couple of decades ago, I really was that young surgeon. I certainly didn't pause afterward to reflect on how I'd acted. That younger surgeon never would have bothered to examine his own behavior. I may still be covered in blemishes, but I'm proud of the fact that I now take the time to examine my worst moments, learn from them, and strive to do better next time.

My evolution from that brash young surgeon into someone more focused on effective leadership and team building has been gradual. It sure didn't happen overnight, but I believe that something changes when you spend so many years devoted to mastering the same tasks. As you seek to master every aspect of the work, you also begin to ask, "What else is there?" You look for ways to improve your methods, your team, and yourself by shining that bright light on every detail of the team as well as you.

The surgeon's headlight isn't the only surgical tool that's a good metaphor for the work of a leader. The surgeon's retractor spreads open the edges of an incision for better exposure and examination; the forceps allow the surgeon to pick up the material or content to be dissected, cut, or removed. The Metzenbaum scissors are the actual instrument for cutting and removing non-valued or beneficial material. And the needle driver and sutures are used for closing up a wound to start the process of healing after dissection. A leader has to be able to slice his or her organization apart, operate on it, dissect the team, resect the parts that need to be removed or improved, and then sew it up and bring everyone back together to heal. None of this is easy; surgery for the surgeon and patient is traumatic.

Once you slice an organization apart, scrutinize it for ways to make it better and remove infected or dysfunctional areas in order to benefit the whole. It's essential that you also sew everything back together. You've got to help your people heal—I've noticed that many leaders don't do this.

If you're going to reorganize things—fire people or give new people titles, or strip titles from other people—then you need to recognize how disruptive and painful this will be for your team. You've essentially ripped a big hole in the organization and perhaps taken something out of the middle, and now you have two edges of a wound that are no longer connected. The edges may be under tension, and

every surgeon reading this knows that wound edges under tension don't heal well.

Maybe you did all that because you had to cut out some dead tissue, or because you had to restructure some toxic part of the organization. That's great, because those are areas that have to be dealt with, but if at the end you fail to bring those edges back together—if you don't seal the torn edges that you've ripped apart—then the organization won't heal. Instead it will *dehisce,* meaning it will fall apart under tension. They'll fall apart without proper healing following a dissection. That happens to physical wounds that haven't been properly tended to, and it happens in relationships. Your job as a leader is to help your team heal from disruption.

Operating—and Leading—from All Vantage Points

The wisdom of the surgeon's toolkit isn't just for surgeons, nor is it just for CEOs or other business leaders running big, high-powered teams. Maybe you're a stay-at-home dad or mom. Maybe you're leading a youth sports team, or a team of just a couple of employees at your office. These lessons are for all of us. The surgeon's toolkit is a set of strategies for paying attention to all the details around us and then tending to them so that we can do our best work on the things that are most important, such as raising children, coaching, and leading businesses. We become champions of our team's goals.

These days the term *surgeon champion* refers to someone who is involved in developing metrics and measuring outcomes for surgery. This is a lot more complicated than it sounds because the question of exactly what we should measure tends to be disputed. Frankly, the medical field measures many things that don't tell us a whole lot about our performance—and fails to measure many things that could be very informative. In other words, we measure things that don't help us deliver better outcomes for the patient. Instead, we should be focused on *aligned excellence.*

Let's say the most important thing in your life is to raise good kids who are responsible citizens in this world. That sounds like a pretty important goal to me—probably the most important one I have. Now let's say you decide to measure your progress toward that goal by evaluating how well your kid ties his shoes. You'll probably end up with a kid who's a world-class shoe-tier, but do you have any information about whether he's a good citizen? You surely don't. That's what often happens in the medical field. If you're a parent, then you probably want to select metrics like your kid's willingness to help others, what classmates say about him, and what decisions he makes at parties. Choose metrics that *align* with what you believe defines a good kid. That's aligned excellence. And it can be measured.

Plenty of us let our kids sit idly by while we make their lunches or do any number of other chores that they could help with. We do this in part because it's usually easier to do it ourselves without trying to explain the task or convince a child to get up and help. While this is typically the easiest approach, it's not the one that most benefits our kids' long-term development. Instead, you can say,

"Hey, help me with this."

"Come join me. Help me get the bread out."

"Help me make it just the way you like it, with just the right amount of peanut butter and jelly."

"Now help me clean up."

In each of these instances, what you're really saying is, *Come take ownership in this process.*

Suddenly you're turning a seemingly humdrum activity into a chance for your child to claim ownership over a part of his or her life. Maybe up until that moment she took her lunch for granted, but now she sees what goes into it. It doesn't magically appear in her backpack; it requires some effort and work. Maybe next time she can do it all by herself. That's a kernel of leadership in the next generation.

No matter who you are, your most important responsibilities probably have more to do with what you do at home than anywhere else. You'll find more on that in our next and final chapter.

Chapter 12

Final Thoughts: Now You Can Operate in a Better Way

During a talk I recently gave in Chicago, I kicked off by posing a few questions to the distinguished surgeon who had invited me to give the lecture.

"Hey, Jim, how many operations did you do last year?" I asked him.

"Four hundred and twenty-one," he replied.

"That's great," I said. "How many of those patients died?"

"Only one."

"That's good, that's good. And how many times did you take your wife out to dinner, and how many of your kid's soccer games did you miss?"

Silence. He didn't have a clue to the last two.

It's not unusual for leaders to become obsessed or overly burdened with success in their professional lives. Nor is it unusual for them to measure their success out to several decimal places. But as I mentioned in the previous chapter, we often fail to measure the right things. Maybe you're someone who is very successful professionally, but do *you* know when you last went out for dinner with your spouse? Or when you last had a heart-to-heart with one of your kids? Or when you last phoned your mom or dad? My dad is ninety-one now, and my mom is eighty-eight. I do my best to call them every day, even if I'm overseas. I have been measuring all of these things since I got married—but the problem was not measuring the right metrics.

I probably wasn't the world's greatest husband, but I tried to be the best I could be, given I was a busy father and surgeon. My wife passed away a few years ago, and while she was alive, I know that I worked a lot. Too much. I also coached about a million Little League baseball, basketball, hockey, and football teams, which was not always her favorite thing. But I also knew that if it had been three weeks since we'd gone out to dinner, then something was wrong, and we took a night to get out of the house together, get a bite to eat, and go to a movie. This is about not losing sight of what's most important. She was the one I was going to grow old with, she was the one I choose to be with—my kids were given to me.

From its very first pages, this book has been about how the rules of the O.R. contain important leadership lessons, whether you're a doctor, a CEO, a parent, or any other type of leader. It's certainly the case that the lessons in this book apply to work and home, a bit like my first book, *Super Performing at Work and Home,* your most important responsibilities, perhaps contrary to what most people think, probably fall into the latter category. The most important thing isn't really your quarterly earnings report, or even your customer feedback; it's what happens at home with the people you love. The people you come home to, the people you work to provide for, and the ones you hope and pray you make proud of the actions you do all day, every day, day after day. If you ask just about anyone what's the most important thing in their lives, they'll probably say family. The problem is that few of us act like it because we spend so much time at work.

You probably spend at least eight or nine hours at work every day, or maybe more like twelve. On top of that, you may bring work home to do at night and on the weekends. We're so busy clocking our work hours and measuring the success of our organizations, even though our top priority should be our performance as parents and spouses, as siblings, and as sons and daughters.

That lecture I gave in Chicago was about work/life balance. I spoke about that because too many of us are high achievers at work at the expense of our lives at home. Oftentimes, we get home only to turn into different people—people who have shorter tempers, or whose focus is stuck elsewhere, back at the office. Our kids often get the worst of us, when they really should get our very best selves.

Who you are at home also matters for how you perform at work. The truth is that it's very difficult to be a good leader if you're not successful at home.

When you're a leader, you inspire other people to make your vision their own. When they hold your vision in their own hearts, you've done your job. That's the real path to making an impact in the world. And in order to achieve that, your vision will probably have to be something bigger than selling widgets. It will have to be bigger than taking home a paycheck at the end of the day. And you will need to be more than a boss or technocrat who puts in the hours; you'll need to constantly strive to be your best self, professionally as well as personally.

One of the first things this book tackled was the idea that leadership begins with an "I." If you aren't dealing with your personal problems, then no one is going to want to follow you. Remember that expertise will only get you so far, and that you've got to take time to work on yourself and develop the qualities that will make you both a smart leader *and* an effective team member. You will need to engage the people around you on a human level, whether those people are your team members, your employees, your executive board, or the people you love most in the world.

The Only Thing that Matters

You probably have a to-do list. I know I do, and I've

discovered that pretty much everyone else does, too. I often ask about these lists when I'm giving a talk.

"Who in this audience has a to-do list?" I say, and every single hand goes up.

That to-do list serves a purpose, of course, but truth is that it's the wrong kind of list. What each of us really should carry around is a list of who and what we want to *be*, not what we have to *do*. Imagine carrying around a list like this one:

I want to be the guy who doesn't yell when the anesthesiologist is late.

I want to be the guy who helps the resident who's shaking and trembling.

I want to be the person my friends call when they're having trouble in their marriages.

I want to be the guy who helps people when they're in trouble, in the operating room or deciding on a better process to improve throughput in their hospital.

This is the stuff that really matters, though we tend to spend so much time executing the items on our to-do list that these higher priorities get relegated to some unspecified time in the future. Just as we often measure the wrong things, we often focus on doing the things that don't really matter.

I used to be motivated by the idea of becoming the world's best thoracic surgeon—whatever that means—it's silly and not even measurable. Well, I worked hard to obtain an international reputation. However, I'm now at the point in my life where I'm starting to think more about my legacy.

What I care about now is getting to the end of each day and passing what I call the mirror test. That's the moment when you look at yourself in the mirror as you brush your teeth at the end of a long day and ask: did I use every minute of today to be the best person I could to others and do the right thing?

We can all get away with doing the wrong thing and justifying it, but you'll never pass the mirror test that way.

It's taken me a lot of practice, and I still mess up sometimes, but on most days, I now take people aside instead of yelling. I say, "I'm disappointed in what you're doing." I am trying not to yell as much. If I keep my voice down and clearly communicate what they're doing wrong and how it needs to be done differently, and if I do so in a way that's really going to motivate them in the future, then I've done the right thing. I want to pass my own mirror test each night, at the end of that day.

The mirror test is a daily reminder of something that I had to do when I went back to school to get my MBA. When I was finishing that program, they suggested we write our own eulogy. Life is fragile, after all; anything could happen to any one of us on any day. What if, God forbid, today were that day for you? Others would summarize your life in three or four paragraphs in the newspaper or on the Internet. What would they say about you? And *are you proud of what you've done with your time on this earth?* **Are these three to four paragraphs what you wanted your life to represent?**

As I wrote this book, I had been at the University of Alabama for twenty years, and we have built one of the best lung surgery programs in the world. We are proud of that, and we are grateful to the institution for affording us the resources to build the program. But at fifty-five, I realized that I'd done everything I could do in this one place. I realized that my life had begun to stagnate. I'd been coming home to the same house for twenty years, and for the past four years I'd lived alone, since Lorraine has passed away. I had done everything I could do at this stage of my life here and feel less and less valued. So, what next?

It would have been easy to stay where I was, of course. Our natural human inclination is to avoid change. But if I stayed in Alabama and resisted change, then I wouldn't pass the mirror test. I was not really challenging myself as much as I could. A leader has to take risks sometimes, or he can't possibly lead a team to greater heights.

I don't want my eulogy to say that I stayed in the same place for forty-plus years. I don't want it to say that I was a big contributor to my field only in the first decade or two of my career. I want to continue to contribute in a way that's commensurate with my ability, and that meant going somewhere else.

I left Alabama to take a job at New York University Langone Health. NYU and New York City is bigger stage, and everything is different. I have been here a year now, and the culture is great. I have new roles that I enjoy and lead a much larger, more diverse team and lead in different ways.

Though I'm no longer motivated by the sole idea of being the "best" thoracic surgeon in the world—which is what every surgeon should aspire to be—I am motivated to be the best surgical *teacher* and the best leader. By the time I die, I would have had the chance to teach hundreds and hundreds of surgeons. And most of our former students are now trained attendings who operate on their own patients on a daily basis, serving hundreds and hundreds of patients every single day and they teach other medical students, residents, fellows, and attendings.

As academic surgeons, the best part of our job is the legacy that we get to leave behind as we teach, if we do it well—I call it the ripple effect—we create a positive influence on other human beings. This is the true value we bring, and it and perhaps only it, has true lasting significance.

That's what great leaders do. The best leaders affect people's lives in a way that creates an ongoing ripple effect that turns into a cultural tidal wave that improves the world at first around them, and then far beyond them.

At the end of the day, that's what life is all about. My

hope is that this book helps you to understand that as early in your life as you can, earlier than I did. We should all struggle to be the best every day in all the roles God has assigned us: son or daughter, brother or sister, student or teacher, husband or wife, father or mother, worker and/or leader—to lead our lives and our families and our teams to be the best, but it does not truly matter if we achieve that goal or not—all that really matters is the honesty of the effort of that pursuit, of the purity of the journey, of the success we had in making a positive difference in this world during the struggle, and the positive influence we left behind in the people and resources around us.

CPSIA information can be obtained
at www.ICGtesting.com
Printed in the USA
LVHW06s1257120918
589913LV00006B/67/P

9 781949 639216